D0726445

The MRCGP Examination

a guide for candidates and teachers

by

Richard Moore FRCGP

Published by

The Royal College of General Practitioners

The Royal College of General Practitioners was founded in 1952, with this object:
"To encourage, foster, and maintain the highest possible standards in general medical practice and for that purpose to take or join with others in taking steps consistent with the charitable nature of that object which may assist towards the same."

Among its responsibilities under its Royal Charter the College is entitled to:
"Encourage the publication by general medical practitioners of research into medical or scientific subjects with a view to the improvement of general medical practice in any field and to undertake or assist others in undertaking such research.

"Diffuse information on all matters affecting general medical practice and establish, print, publish, issue and circulate such papers, journals, magazines, books, periodicals, and publications and hold such meetings, conferences, seminars, and instructional courses as may assist the object of the College."

@ Royal College of General Practitioners 1994

Second impression 1994

Published by the Exeter Publications Office
Royal College of General Practitioners
9 Marlborough Road
Exeter, Devon EX2 4TJ.

Printed by Hobbs the Printers of Southampton
Cover design by ADP Ltd, Tiverton

ISBN 0 85084 193 3

Contents

Editor's Preface

The history of the development of the MRCGP examination, set against the history of the development of the College itself, has already been described in a College publication—*Occasional Paper 46* (RCGP, 1990) but this is the first time the College has published a book of practical help to candidates. Publication of such a book is both welcome and timely as it not only looks back, advising on the present—how to take the examination now—but looks forward to its development in the future.

The big question which has never been fully answered is why take the examination? There are in fact five reasons why general practitioners should take the MRCGP examination, which is still a voluntary choice in this country, and these reasons need to be clearly understood so that everybody is aware of the complex issues which are involved.

1 Personal satisfaction

The General Medical Council is the governing body of the whole of the medical profession and it recognizes only one British "additional registrable qualification" in general medical practice—this is the MRCGP. There is no other way in which a doctor who has chosen to be a general practitioner in the UK can obtain a higher qualification in his or her subject other than by passing this examination. As shown in this book, it is an examination which has been rigorously developed since 1965 (RCGP, 1990) and which has been subjected to the most severe critical analysis in its methods and techniques. *The Lancet* (1990) has commented that among the Royal Colleges the Royal College of General Practitioners comes out well in the degree of openness with which it approaches its examination and the rationale for the way it is constructed.

It follows, therefore, that there is considerable professional pride for young doctors who, having completed vocational training for general practice, obtain the seal of approval from their Royal College that they have reached an appropriate standard to be an unsupervised principal in general practice.

It is not only a matter of pride for trainees but also for trainers, course organizers and regional advisers who play an important part in the individual and collective performance of trainees. Some training practices have an outstanding record in the MRCGP examination, with 100%, or near 100%, achievement of their trainees and this often reflects high quality teaching in the practice and sustained educational support throughout the trainee year.

2 Career advancement

The second reason for taking the examination is either to prepare the way or to support the doctor in terms of professional advancement in his or her chosen career in general practice. It has been known for many years that the MRCGP is effectively compulsory for those who aspire to hold leading positions within the general practice branch of the profession; for example, all the professors of general practice and regional advisers are College members, as are virtually all the associate advisers and the great majority of course organizers. In some regions the MRCGP is required for those who wish to have the privilege of becoming trainers. Some university departments of general practice will only appoint research fellows who have satisfied the examiners of the Royal College as to their clinical competence.

However, all these positions form a relative minority among the general practice branch of the profession, which numbers 30,000 in the United Kingdom. The real issue in terms of career advancement is whether or not the MRCGP will be required for appointment as a principal in general practice. There are a number of reasons why this needs to be thought about and this policy is moving up the national agenda swiftly at the time of writing of this book.

First, it is important to remember that in every other branch of medical practice doctors are individually assessed by the appropriate Royal College or Faculty on their chosen subject. In the past such assessment was effectively required before appointment as a consultant and the Royal Colleges have assessors on consultant appointment selection committees. However, in recent years the system has changed and most of the Royal Colleges and specialist Faculties now require possession of the appropriate Royal College diploma before *entry* for training. Thus, for example, the MRCP is effectively required before a doctor can enrol as a registrar in medicine and the FRCS is required for *entry* to training programmes in surgery.

Against this background it becomes increasingly anomalous that in the largest branch of the profession doctors should not be systematically examined by their own Royal College, particularly at the end of a period of training which alone is statutory and governed by Act of Parliament.

It was in 1979 that a key policy was developed by the last Royal Commission to examine the National Health Service in Britain. The crucial paragraph 7.29 reads:

> ... but, as in other specialties, experience in itself will not be a sufficient indication of quality of performance—it will need to be tested and competence demonstrated. As with hospital specialties possession of the postgraduate qualification of the relevant Royal College should become the norm for appointment as a principal in general practice [in the NHS].

This paragraph attracted relatively little attention at the time. However, it was finally examined by the Royal College of General Practitioners in May 1993 when its Council formally adopted this policy. Thus it is now the policy of the College that in future all those who are to hold unsupervised responsibility as principals in general practice in the National Health Service should hold the MRCGP.

The College does not of itself have the power to introduce this ruling. Ultimately either family health services authorities or the Department of Health will need to adopt the policy. However, previous College policies of this kind have been followed by implementation usually within about 12 years: for example, the College policy urging the introduction of vocational training (CGP, 1965) was implemented by Act of Parliament in 1977, and similarly its policy on the care of children (RCGP, 1978) was implemented in the 1990 General Practitioner Contract. It must therefore be assumed that sooner or later this examination will be required for entry as a principal and the only question now is not whether but when.

In fact the speed of change in the National Health Service at present is such that implementation of this new policy may well come much faster than the previous 12-year period. For years many practices have quietly insisted that only members will be shortlisted for principalships and a growing number of family health services authorities are now doing the same for single-handed vacancies. This trend is likely to continue and the profession has great power in its own hands since most principalships are filled by practices themselves.

3 Quality marker

As if these professional pressures were not enough, other developments in society are also focusing attention on possession of the MRCGP as a marker of quality. The decision by the General Medical Council to erase from the register a young doctor who held the JCPTGP certificate but whose diabetic patient died has led to serious questions about the degree of guarantee that the JCPTGP certificate (unsupported by an MRCGP) offers patients; and in a television programme in October 1993, comment was made on the performance of a few unfortunate general practitioners who it was alleged had made clinical errors, as to whether or not they possessed the MRCGP. This led to patients ringing the Royal College to find out how they could identify whether or not their own family doctor held this qualification.

At the very beginning of the College's history, a famous early leader of the College, Fraser Rose, made the much quoted statement that people were joining the College at that time "not because we are better doctors, but because we wish to become better doctors". This marvellous phrase has rung through the ages since that time but now in the early 1990s it may be starting to become out of date.

Evidence is steadily accumulating that general practitioners who are members of the College are in a number of ways different from those who are not. As early as 1967, Cartwright found that members were better equipped, offered a wider range of services and had a deeper understanding of the psychiatric aspects of general practice. More recently it has been found that general practitioners who are members are significantly less likely to be reprimanded or erased by the General Medical Council or to be found in breach of their terms of service by the National Health Service (DoH, 1988; personal communication). If these early reports stand the test of time then a situation may soon arise when the MRCGP comes increasingly to be seen as a quality marker, a badge signalling to patients a higher likelihood of competence-- although of course this will never mean that there are not some outstandingly good general practitioners who are not members of the College.

4 Financial advantage

The actual cost to the individual doctor of becoming a member of the College is a tax allowable expense which may be channelled either through the practice account (preferable if all partners are members) or personally, but in either event will attract tax relief for the doctor at his or her highest rate (25% or 40% at the time of writing).

There is another possibility for saving costs which has also recently become available for College members (*General Practitioner*, 1991). In 1991 it became possible for members to join a new professional indemnity service offered by the Medical Insurance Agency. The insurance premium for MRCGPs is now less than that for non MRCGPs with a difference greater than the annual cost of the College's subscription; so that payment of the annual indemnity premium means that for a growing number of College members their whole annual subscription to the College (£225 pa in 1993) is effectively free.

If claims against doctors continue to rise and if College members' premiums continue to justify a differential, possessing the MRCGP could become increasingly financially advantageous.

5 Supporting the discipline

The final reason for being a member of the College is simply that it is part of the collective, professional responsibility of general practitioners to support the only Royal College they have in their subject. Whereas there are often multiple specialist Colleges for one discipline (there is a Royal College of Physicians of Edinburgh, a Royal College of Physicians and Surgeons of Glasgow, a Royal College of Physicians of London, and a Royal College of Physicians in Ireland) there is for general practitioners in the United Kingdom only one national academic body which can represent their interests.

The College is a voluntary body and, as its accounts reveal, it is heavily dependent on subscriptions for its income (RCGP, 1993). About three-quarters of all the working money in the College depends on the subscriptions of members and without these general practitioners would be substantially less well represented. College subscriptions support about 100 general practitioners who represent general practice on a whole variety of other organizations. The voice of general practice has always been dangerously thin on the ground and is still seriously stretched— often the College representative is the only general practitioner in the room. Some highly prestigious organizations, notably the Conference of Medical Royal Colleges and Faculties in the United Kingdom, are such that the General Medical Services Committee could never aspire to attend, so that the whole thrust of representation of the biggest branch of the medical profession depends on the College member appointed by the Council to speak for all of us.

This network of representation, which operates both nationally and locally, forms an important bulwark in preventing hostile policies and arrangements being thrust on general practice. There can be no doubt that membership of the College plays an important role in making sure the voice of general practice is heard in every arena.

The effectiveness of the College as a stimulus for change and development is already well proved. It was the College that devised and developed the first scientific journal of general practice in the world which today ranks in the first 20 among the medical journals in the USA citation index (SCI, 1991); it was the College whose work led to the introduction of the Vocational Training Act; and it was the College that devised and developed the first registrable postgraduate qualification in general practice—the MRCGP examination. All of this had to be done by general practitioners for general practitioners.

Nor should it be forgotten that the College offers support to the individual not just the discipline as a whole. One of the great strengths of the College is that there is a regional organization and there is a faculty of the College in every part of the United Kingdom, and an overseas faculty as well. The faculties run local meetings, lectures and varying special interest groups for members, offering support in a way that could not be done centrally.

Finally, as Richard Moore writes, membership of the College alone admits a general practitioner to entry for the College's Fellowship by Assessment scheme, the leading quality assurance programme in British general practice.

Conclusion

Although some of these issues have yet to be finally clarified, it can be seen that there are powerful reasons why young doctors should take the examination and that the best advice that anyone can now give to a younger colleague pursuing a career in general practice is to take the examination and remain associated with the College thereafter.

This book is the third in the series of practical workbooks published by the College and anyone wishing to become a member of the College by examination will find it an invaluable source of information, not only on how to prepare for it but also how to tackle it when the time comes. Written by an experienced College examiner the book should make its own valuable contribution to the development not only of the examination but of the College itself.

DENIS PEREIRA GRAY
Honorary Editor
College Publications

November 1993

References

Cartwright A (1967) *Patients and their Doctors.* London, Routledge & Kegan Paul.

College of General Practitioners (1965) *Special Vocational Training for General Practice. Report from General Practice 1.* London, CGP

General Practitioner (1991) 6 April.

Lancet (1990) Examining the Royal Colleges' examinations. Editorial, **335**, 443.

Royal College of General Practitioners (1978) The care of children. *Journal of the Royal College of General Practitioners* **28**, 553–6.

Royal College of General Practitioners (1990) *Examination for Membership of the Royal College of General Practitioners (MRCGP). Occasional Paper 46.* Ed. Lockie C. London, RCGP.

Royal College of General Practitioners (1993) Honorary Treasurer's Report. In *RCGP Members' Reference Book.* London. Sterling. p. 88.

Royal Commission on the National Health Service (1979) Report. London, HMSO. para 7.29.

Scientific Citation Index (1991) IV. Subject category lisiting: Journals ranked by impact factor within category. USA, Journal Citation Reports.

Preface

The text of this handbook originally appeared as a series of articles for *The Practitioner* which were published between September 1991 and May 1993. I would like to acknowledge the kind permission, readily given by *The Practitioner* and its publisher Morgan Grampian Ltd, to use that text as the foundation of this book. The articles have been thoroughly revised and edited to avoid duplication, and have been brought up to date to include the changes that have occurred in the examination recently or are planned for the near future.

It is entirely fitting that *The Practitioner* should have been the vehicle for this publication, for when it was founded in 1868 it was a vital source of news and information for our predecessors in general practice who were isolated by time and distance from their colleagues, and it was a voice that could speak independently from the specialists who then tightly controlled medical education. Later, in the gloom of post-war Britain and at the time of radical change as the National Health Service was introduced, *The Practitioner* spoke out forcefully in support of the foundation of a College of General Practitioners. Not only did it celebrate the College's foundation in a series of leading articles (*Practitioner*, 1953a,b), but it also published the newly founded institution's first Annual Report as a Supplement in November 1953 (*Practitioner* 1953c). The Founding Officers were Dr G F Abercrombie, Chairman; Dr F M Rose, Vice-Chairman; and Dr J H Hunt, Honorary Secretary. It was Dr Fraser Rose who, as Chairman of the Examination Committee in 1954, laid the foundations of the examination for membership of the Royal College of General Practitioners as we know it today, and it is his name which is remembered in the Fraser Rose Medal awarded to the candidate gaining the highest marks in the examination.

I would also like to acknowledge the help and inspiration which many people have given me in writing this book and, it is to be hoped, have thereby contributed to the possibility of a wider understanding of the MRCGP examination, its purpose and its methods.

Many colleagues have shown great interest and given me much encouragement, and in the writing of the original articles Miranda Hart and Clare Griffith of the editorial staff of *The Practitioner* were very helpful and full of ideas. It was Dr Cameron Lockie, of the Editorial Board of *The Practitioner*, who originally suggested that the articles might form the basis of a book. Professor Lesley Southgate, Convenor of the Panel of Examiners, read the early drafts and I am especially grateful to her for the advice and support that she has given. Similarly Dr John Toby, who was Chairman of the Examination Board at the time the book was being written and whose contribution to the examination has been so notable, has commended the project and given much helpful advice.

Drs Declan Dwyer, Roger Neighbour, Peter Tate, and Julian Turner have all read the drafts of chapters describing the various sections of the examination for which they are the convenors, and I am particularly grateful to Dr Roger Neighbour for supplying his observations on the MEQ questions, which are reproduced here with the permission of *The Practitioner*, where they have also appeared: also to Professor Ian Stanley for guidance on the matter of accreditation: and to Mr Tom Dastur, Head of the College's Examination Department, for much assistance and advice and for correcting the drafts of early chapters; also for supplying the various documents reproduced in the book.

Finally, and by no means least, I must thank Professor Denis Pereira Gray for much support and encouragement in the production of this book. I am grateful to him not only for his much valued contribution of the Editor's Preface but also for helpful advice.

Notwithstanding the quality of the advice referred to above, it should be emphasized that this book represents my personal views, based on my experience as an examiner for the Royal College of General Practitioners since 1984, and for ten years as Course

Organizer for the Shrewsbury Vocational Training Scheme. I have been advised on matters of fact by the Convenor of the Panel of Examiners and the convenors of each section of the examination. I believe that the statements and opinions expressed in the book fairly represent the state of the examination at the time of writing, but they should not be taken as the official policy of the Panel of Examiners, nor of the College. Other publications, notably *Occasional Paper 46* (RCGP, 1990) and documents circulated within the College, may be consulted for an account of the examination from the responsible authorities.

Similarly, because it is not the purpose of this book to teach the knowledge and skills which the examination tests, and to avoid the possibility that it might be seen as setting a syllabus for the examination, no reading list has been included. However, a very comprehensive Reading and Reference Book List for General Practice has been prepared by the Vale of Trent Faculty of the College and can be purchased from the Vale of Trent Faculty, RCGP Postgraduate Office, Medical School, Queen's Medical Centre, Nottingham.

I am pleased to acknowledge, too, the contribution made by Anne, my wife, who has not only tolerated the distractions and peculiarities of a would-be author but has subdued our rebellious wordprocessor into a state of disciplined and subservient co-operation.

Finally, and by no means least, I wish to show my appreciation of two groups of doctors essential to the examination. One is the Panel of Examiners, who are such good companions and dedicated colleagues, from whom I have learned much. The other and most important, is all those candidates, past and future, whose commitment to the standards explicit in the examination is the seed-corn of the future success of the Royal College of General Practitioners. To them this book is dedicated.

I thank them all.

October 1993   RICHARD MOORE

References

Practitioner (1953a) College of General Practitioners. Editorial, **170**, 1–2.

Practitioner (1953b) College of General Practitioners. Editorial, **170**, 105–6.

Practitioner (1953c) First Annual Report of the College of General Practitioners. **170**, Suppl. 1–32.

Royal College of General Practitioners (1990) *Examination for Membership of the Royal College of General Practitioners. Development, Current State and Future Trends. Occasional Paper 46.* Ed. Lockie C. London, RCGP.

Note about the author

The author is a Member of the Panel of Examiners of the Royal College of General Practitioners and Medical Facilitator of the Shropshire Medical Audit Advisory Group. He was formerly a General Practitioner in Shrewsbury and Course Organizer for the Shrewsbury Vocational Training Scheme.

1 Historical Background

Every year nearly two thousand candidates take the examination for Membership of the Royal College of General Practitioners. Their reasons are mostly to demonstrate the satisfactory completion of their training, but there are a variety of other motivations too. This book describes the purpose, structure and development of the examination so that prospective candidates can direct their studies most appropriately, not only for the examination but also for their subsequent careers. It is also hoped that it will be of interest to others who are concerned with promoting and maintaining high educational and professional standards in general medical practice.

Foundation of a College

The concept of education for, and examination in the discipline of general practice dates from as early as the 1840s, when registration for medical practitioners was being debated and introduced. Plans to found a College of General Practitioners were put forward but did not find universal approval. An early proponent was William Gaitskell, President of the Metropolitan Society of General Practitioners in Medicine and Surgery, who wrote to *The Lancet* in 1830 saying: "Various branches of the medical profession have colleges, charters and corporations, from which the general practitioner is either altogether excluded, or attached as an appendage only; he is not admitted to a participation in their councils, or to share in their honours; as a general practitioner, he belongs to no one branch, and is, therefore, virtually excluded from all" (*Practitioner*, 1953a).

1

A few years later, Dr James Cole of Bewdley in Worcestershire, writing in the *Provincial Medical and Surgical Journal*, proposed a remedy for the educational subservience of his part of the medical profession. This was the "incorporation of the eighteen thousand Licentiates of the Hall [of Apothecaries] into a Royal College of Apothecaries ... By this means we obtain ... a clearly defined, well and thoroughly educated body of Medical Practitioners who shall be in every way worthy of the respect of their colleagues and of public confidence". In the same year correspondence in *The Lancet* was lively, with proposals for the foundation of a "royal college of general practitioners in medicine, surgery and midwifery", and "The College of Medicine and Surgery". Calls from all over the country supported the idea, expressed by Dr George Ross of Kennington, who wrote in *The Lancet* in 1844: "The laws of the College of Surgeons are made for the Council and Fellows. Let them retain their privileges and retain the honours of their institution; but let the general practitioner have also his college—he has interests to support and a respectability to uphold; let him therefore possess the means of accomplishing these things" (*Practitioner*, 1953a). The British Medical Association supported the proposals, saying that it was "imperatively necessary" to form a "legal union of the general practitioners in this kingdom into a distinct corporation", and this indeed did happen with the formation of a National Association of General Practitioners in Medicine, Surgery, and Midwifery. The purpose of this was to petition for a Charter of Incorporation and might well have succeeded but for its rather ineffective organization. Parliament was debating medical reform, and a College of General Practitioners was included in one of the Bills before Parliament. Unfortunately confusion surrounded the whole movement; support was vociferous from London but less so from the provinces, and the voice of the College of Surgeons, which was reluctant to yield its educational power, prevailed over the pleas of a disorganized and divided profession, and the proposals foundered.

One hundred years later the foundation of the National Health Service in 1948 led to a crisis amongst general practitioners who were starved of resources, experienced serious loss of income, and were overwhelmed by the public's expectation of free treatment. The determination of a small but dedicated group of doctors rekindled the enthusiasm of the profession to take responsibility for its own education and development. It had lacked control of its own destiny for too long "without headquarters, without academic leadership of its own, without much influence over undergraduate or postgraduate teaching, and without the status of their specialist colleagues" (Fry et al., 1982).

The determination and foresight of Dr John Hunt, Dr Fraser Rose and others who were unaware of the failures of a hundred years before but who encountered opposition from their specialist colleagues as forceful as that which faced their predecessors were successfully rewarded with the foundation in 1953 of the College of General Practitioners, later to become a Royal College by command of Her Majesty Queen Elizabeth II in 1967.

Membership examination

The objectives of the College are: "To encourage, foster and maintain the highest possible standards in general practice, and for that purpose take any steps which may assist towards the same." Its Charter also permits it to grant diplomas and certificates of proficiency in general medical practice. To meet these obligations the Membership Examination was introduced in 1965, whose purpose was, and still is, to demonstrate that applicants for membership have indeed reached the standard required for membership. However, with the introduction of mandatory training for general practice whose regulations have until recently not specified any nationally standardized end-point assessment, the majority of candidates are now doctors completing their vocational training who see it as a means of motivating their studies and demonstrating their abilities to prospective partners as well as a way of entering the College. There are still many candidates, however, who are established principals with an enthusiasm for education and assessment, or are prospective trainers, teachers and examiners.

From the general public's point of view, examinations may be seen as a guarantee of quality, though most of the Royal Colleges do not provide enough information for that judgement to be made (*Lancet*, 1990). However, the Royal College of General Practitioners

3

is said by *The Lancet* to be an "honourable exception" in that it does publish enough information to enable interested parties to judge the adequacy of the examination. Indeed it is under constant review to ensure its reliability and validity, and welcomes visitors to observe the examination in progress. The *British Medical Journal* has published a series of articles describing the examinations of the Royal Colleges and the account of the MRCGP comments favourably on the College's confidence in accepting such outside scrutiny (Godlee, 1991).

Before the examination became compulsory for membership of the College in 1968, there were various ways in which aspiring members could qualify, based mainly on relevant experiences and including either the possession of a higher postgraduate degree or diploma or the promise to accept "postgraduate instruction for three days each year or an equivalent number of hours" (*Practitioner*, 1953b). With the hindsight of forty years the word 'instruction' rather than 'education', and the idea that possession of a diploma removes the need to promise to continue education, seem strangely anachronistic. There had always been an intention to institute an examination, and the first took place in 1965, thirteen years after the College's foundation. There were five candidates all of whom were successful. Now there are about a thousand or more candidates in May and six or seven hundred in October, of whom about three quarters are successful.

It is probably the largest and most comprehensive examination for doctors in primary care in the world. Various systems exist in other countries. In the United States of America, for example, six thousand primary care physicians take the accreditation examination each year, but this consists only of a 750-question multiple choice question paper. The Royal Colleges of General Practitioners of Australia and of New Zealand both have clinical components to their examinations, as does the College of Family Physicians of Canada, but all have many fewer candidates (Wakeford, 1990). In the UK until now there has been no clinical component, because the large number of candidates poses problems of logistics, consistency and reliability; but this matter, which some see as a weakness, is being addressed (see Chapter 15).

4

Components of the examination

The MRCGP examination consists of five parts, three written and two oral. In addition, before candidates are accepted for entry, they must produce two 'Certificates of Competence', one in cardiopulmonary resuscitation, and the other in child health surveillance. The written parts of the examination comprise a multiple choice question paper (MCQ) with 360 items of the true/false type and the new extended matching questions which test factual knowledge; a modified essay question paper (MEQ), to assess problem-solving and clinical management skills; and a critical reading question paper (CRQ) to examine the ability to comprehend and respond to written material and communication. The two oral examinations are each of half an hour duration and are designed to assess competence in clinical, managerial and educational areas and to assess the breadth, consistency, and rationality of the candidates' attitudes and thinking. The first oral is based upon a practice experience questionnaire (PEQ), which candidates submit on entry, outlining the nature of the practices in which they have been working while preparing for the examination and listing a collection of cases they have managed. This does not form part of the examination as such and does not generate marks, but enables the examiners to ask questions of direct relevance to the candidates' experience.

The methods of the examination and the techniques of the examiners are under continuous review and development. In 1986/87 its structure was considered in detail by Dr David Swanson (1987), an American psychometrician, who commended the system as it then was and advised on areas where change was desirable. The challenge was taken up and under the guidance of the Centre for Medical Education of the University of Dundee various changes were made. One of the principal aims was to improve the reliability of the examination, that is to say that if a candidate were to take the same examination again the result would also be the same. This is measured by a statistical formula known as the alpha coefficient, where 1.0 is ideal and 0.8 or more is acceptable. The recent MRCGP papers have been shown to be over the 0.8 level. A major change was the abandonment of the old essay style papers in favour of the critical reading question papers, which are not only more discriminating and relevant but more reliable too.

The oral examinations have also been carefully re-assessed and refined. The selection of oral questions has been directed into seven 'areas of competence' to ensure a set of tests which covers the whole range of practice without duplication. Marking has been made more objective and techniques of examination more discriminating. The old 'log diary' was revised and made relevant to modern practice, and renamed the 'practice experience questionnaire'. Future developments will be guided by the researchers of the University of Cambridge Local Examinations Syndicate.

The examiners

The examiners are all members or fellows of the College and are proposed as examiners through the faculty structure. Many, but not all, of them are doctors who have a special interest in continuing medical education as trainers, tutors, course organizers or regional advisers, and some are in academic posts. Prospective new examiners must have passed the examination themselves, and if they have not done so recently they must be prepared to take the papers again. The initial assessment of potential new examiners consists of two days' observing the examinations and an assessment day involving group work, mock oral examination and information about the examination and its processes. By no means all who are proposed are finally selected.

All examiners continue training throughout their time on the panel, with regular observer periods and subsequent critical discussions, feedback on their marking performance, videorecording and analysis of their oral examinations, as well as discussion of techniques, policies and developments at the annual three-day workshop. There are currently about 120 examiners.

Lines of accountability

The Panel of Examiners takes its authority from the Council of the College through the Examination Board of Council, the chairman of which is a member of Council and usually an examiner. Other members of the Board are the Convenor of the Panel of Examiners, members appointed by Council, elected representatives of the panel and the convenors of the various examination components who are observers. The whole process is administered by lay personnel in the Examination Department, who also manage the computer systems for administrative applications, for marking, and for processing results.

Sitting the examination

The examination takes place twice a year. Papers can be written at various places throughout the United Kingdom, and at Dublin in the Republic of Ireland and Sennelager in Germany. Candidates who achieve marks in the papers above a certain level (approximately one standard deviation below the mean) are invited to the oral examination six weeks later in either London or Edinburgh. The results are published as soon as all the orals have been completed, and candidates are informed of the results by post.

The scope of the MRCGP

The outstanding achievement of the College in its early years was a widespread acceptance of the belief that general practice is a medical discipline in its own right, requiring basic and continuing education, self-esteem among its practitioners, and recognition and respect from colleagues in other disciplines. In doing so it has realized the aspirations of our predecessors of 150 years ago. The discipline of general practice, developed in this way, is a very wide one embracing aspects of many others. By the same token the subject of the examination covers the whole range of activities in general medical practice in the United Kingdom, including those areas which overlap with other disciplines and professions. This is an important point, for it is not merely a test of clinical knowledge or diagnostic skill but also includes assessment of candidates' abilities in consulting and communication skills and practice management, and of their attitudes in areas such as ethics and medical politics. It is not prescriptive in this respect and does not dictate a syllabus; rather, it seeks to enquire whether candidates have a rational basis for the beliefs they hold and the actions they propose such as to achieve the standards demanded of members of a professional College.

The agenda for such education was set out in the College's publication *The Future General Practitioner—Learning and Teaching* (RCGP, 1972). This fundamental report defined the programme for education for general practice and referred to a general practitioner as "a doctor who provides personal primary and continuing care to individuals and families ... ", and whose "diagnoses are composed in physical, psychological and social terms". Such doctors "work in a team and delegate when necessary ... " and "intervene educationally, preventively and therapeutically to promote ... health". That is the basis of general practice in Great Britain at the end of the twentieth century, and on that basis the examination is offered to its candidates.

References

Fry J, Hunt JH and Pinsent RJFH (1982) *A History of the Royal College of General Practitioners. The First 25 Years.* Lancaster, MTP Press.

Godlee F (1991) MRCGP: examining the exam. *British Medical Journal* **303**, 235–8.

Lancet (1990) Examining the Royal Colleges' examinations. Editorial, **335**, 443.

Practitioner (1953a) Report of Foundation Council of the College of General Practitioners. **170**, Suppl. 1–32.

Practitioner (1953b) College of General Practitioners. Editorial, **170**, 1–2.

Royal College of General Practitioners (1972) *The Future General Practitioner—Learning and Teaching.* London, British Medical Journal.

Swanson DB (1987) Review of Membership Examination Procedures of the Royal College of General Practitioners. Unpublished.

Tombleson P and Wakeford R (1989) Why do trainees take the membership examination? *Journal of the Royal College of General Practitioners* **39**, 168–71.

Wakeford R (1990) International background. In *Examination for Membership of the Royal College of General Practitioners. Occasional Paper 46.* Ed. Lockie C. London, Royal College of General Practitioners. pp 4–9.

2 Eligibility and Entry for the Examination

The purpose of the Royal College of General Practitioners is to be an "Academic body, with broad educational aims ... [and] the headquarters of general practitioners in Great Britain, and to help and encourage them to maintain a high standard" (General Practice Steering Committee, 1953). It therefore follows that its members will be those who have already become general practitioners or are eligible to be so as a result of appropriate training. In this respect the MRCGP examination differs from the examinations of most of the other Royal Colleges, whose aims are to test the competence of doctors embarking upon higher professional training. The MRCGP examination, on the other hand, tests competence at the end of training.

Eligibility

Candidates for membership, and therefore for the examination, must:

1. Be fully registered medical practitioners who have completed, or who will complete within eight weeks of the date of the oral examination, three years' full-time, or equivalent part-time, post-registration experience which:

   (i) includes not less than two years in general practice (including any periods as a trainee practitioner)

   or

   (ii) includes one year as a trainee practitioner and two years of full-time medical experience all within the United Kingdom and Republic of Ireland, or as specially recognized by the College.

10

2. Pass the examination in accordance with Ordnance 3 of the College's Royal Charter.

There is a rider added to the conditions of membership which requires all doctors aspiring to membership to give an undertaking, if admitted, to "uphold and promote the aims of the College to the best of his or her ability, and while a member of the College and in active practice, to undertake approved postgraduate study". This is, of course, no more than would be expected of any professional person in active practice.

Associateship

It is worth noting that associateship of the College is available to doctors who have not yet gained the necessary qualification or experience for membership, or who do not wish to sit the examination but do wish to enjoy the benefits which the College has to offer. However, they may not designate themselves as members, nor may they vote at general meetings.

Application procedures

The examination takes place twice a year, with the papers being written in May and October and the orals following about six weeks later for those whose marks in the papers are sufficient. (Approximately 15% of candidates are excluded at this stage because their marks are too low.) The details of dates and locations are published from time to time in the *British Journal of General Practice*, or may be obtained on enquiry at the College. The places where the written examinations are held are given in Table 2.1.

Application is made on a form obtainable from the Examination Department, Royal College of General Practitioners, 14 Princes Gate, London SW7 1PU by the date specified for each diet, which is not less than eight weeks before the date of the papers, that is by early March for the May examination and late August for the one in October. Application well before the deadline is recommended. The form, which seeks details about training and experience, is reproduced in Appendix 1.

11

Table 2.1 Places where the written examinations are held

England		Republic of	
	London	**Ireland**	Dublin
	Birmingham		
	Bristol		
	Liverpool	**Scotland**	Edinburgh
	Manchester		
	Newcastle upon Tyne	**Wales**	Cardiff
	Ripon		
Northern Ireland	Belfast	**Germany**	Sennelager

Endorsement

Candidates who enter the examination before the end of their vocational training or less than one year after completing it must have their applications endorsed by someone in authority in their training programmes. These include the postgraduate dean, regional adviser, associate adviser and course organizer. Early attention to the completion of these certificates is advisable, as they may take some time to process when perhaps a hundred or more applications are being made in a region. Delay in obtaining the necessary signatures is not accepted by the examination authority as a reason for late entry.

Fee

The fee at the time of writing (1993–4) is £295, a small sum in relation to the 10-year long training of a general practitioner. The College's policy regarding the examination application fee is to set it at a level which will cover all the direct and indirect costs of running the examination, including maintenance of the Examination Board and its various working groups, and the examination development consultancy services. The fee must be returned with the application form.

12

Dates of orals

Candidates are informed in writing of the provisional dates on which they will be called to the orals, if appropriate, at the time they sit the papers. As these dates are unchangeable except in absolute emergency, candidates are asked to inform the Examination Department at the time of application if a date for the orals is likely to be impossible.

Acceptance of entry

On receipt of the completed application form, the entrance fee and certificates in child health surveillance and cardiopulmonary resuscitation (see below), the candidate's eligibility for membership is assessed against the entry requirements. If eligible, he or she will receive acknowledgement of acceptance and a complimentary package of past examination papers.

Practice experience questionnaire

Shortly after this, instructions relating to the written examination, together with a practice experience questionnaire (PEQ), are sent to candidates, who must complete the PEQ and return it to the College by a specified date, usually four to five weeks before the oral examinations.

The questionnaire seeks details of the practice in which the candidate has prepared for the examination but does not generate any marks in itself, nor is it used in any way to assess training practices. Its purpose is to provide a basis on which questions in the first oral examination can be chosen that are directly relevant to the candidates' experience and practical work. The PEQ will be discussed in more detail in Chapter 4.

Precertification

Precertification in cardiopulmonary resuscitation and child health surveillance was introduced after much debate because of the need to demonstrate basic competence in these areas despite the difficulties presented by the logistics of examining two thousand candidates a year. To do so at the time of the examination would require enormous resources in space, equipment and examination time. The skills needed are not peculiar to general practice, and indeed it could be argued that they are better taught and assessed by people other than general practice examiners. It was therefore decided to delegate this part of the examination to others.

Although it could be argued that both these areas are integral parts of general practice and should be assessed as part of the examination like other skills, there are important differences which justify the distinction from other topics and these are discussed below.

Cardiopulmonary resuscitation

Cardiopulmonary resuscitation (CPR) can be a dramatic intervention in cardiac arrest when carried out correctly (Pai et al., 1987) and clearly it is a skill that anyone likely to be involved in the care of people at risk should have, as indeed should members of the public. However, there is evidence that even though the skills have been properly taught and learned they deteriorate quickly if not practised (Lowenstein et al., 1981; Vincent et al., 1984; David and Prior-Willeard, 1993). The Examination Board therefore determined that the credibility of the examination would be diminished if some evidence of proficiency in this area was not included, and to avoid the problems inherent in testing it at the examination venue decided to delegate this function to others with the necessary equipment and expertise and with a nationwide presence.

The authorities who are approved for testing are shown in Table 2.2 and include doctors with special experience such as consultant anaesthetists, casualty consultants and members of BASICS. Ambulance service training and testing centres are also approved and are willing to provide this service. Addresses are included in the Notes for Candidates which are sent to all applicants (Appendix 2).

Ideally the testing should be done with a computerized system for measuring effectiveness (the Laerdal Skill Meter), but a personally observed test using predetermined criteria is acceptable.

Table 2.2 Authorities approved for the issue of certificates in cardiopulmonary resuscitation skills (CPR) for the MRCGP examination.

- Ambulance Service Training and Testing Centres (for addresses see Appendix 2).

- The following doctors, who are also members of the Resuscitation Council:
  - General practitioners
  - Consultants
  - Medical members of the Red Cross or St John Ambulance
  - Members of the British Association for Immediate Care (BASICS)
  - Members of the Casualty Surgeons Association

When this requirement was first introduced some doctors objected to being taught and tested by persons such as ambulance officers who were not medically qualified. However, there is no organization better qualified to teach and test these skills than those whose duty it is to carry out cardiopulmonary resuscitation frequently, and who have the nationwide organization and equipment to do this consistently and efficiently. In practice a sizeable proportion of candidates continue to be tested by ambulance personnel, although the majority are certificated by hospital consultants (Dastur T, personal communication).

An advantage for the candidate of doing the tests before the actual examination is that in the event of an inadequate performance in the test, further instruction may be given and the test retaken at the same time. If the tests were done at the MRCGP examination venue, that would not be possible and candidates who might otherwise have been successful could fail.

A fee may be charged by those who teach and test resuscitation skills and provide the certificates. This is payable by the candidate and does not form part of the entry fee. The certificates must also be provided on the approved form and be submitted by the closing date for the receipt of application for the examination. The form of the necessary certificate is shown in Appendix 2.

Child health surveillance

A similar system of precertification is used for the purposes of child health surveillance (CHS). Here again it was thought that to have a mandatory section on the subject in every examination would be inadequate to test the necessary skills, and exclude some other possible topic to the detriment of the examination's reliability. In the case of child health surveillance certificates, those authorized to sign are general practitioners approved for CHS services by family health services authorities (FHSAs) and health boards, and consultants and community paediatricians who undertake CHS work. The possession of the MRCGP by examination demonstrates competence in child health surveillance, and successful candidates will therefore be acceptable by FHSAs and health boards for CHS services. The appropriate certificate is reproduced in Appendix 3.

Who takes the examination?

At present about 80% of candidates are trainees and of the remainder many have recently finished their training. Others have delayed their entry to the College for a variety of reasons, or may have special reasons for sitting the examination such as to become a trainer, course organizer—or even an examiner. A review of the reasons given by trainees for taking the examination (Tombleson and Wakeford, 1989) showed that 71% saw success in the examination as a help in getting a job; a similar proportion (67%) said that it provided a desirable discipline in their vocational training. Similarly 66% believed that the examination's most important role was to ensure a basic level of competence before supervision during training ceased. This is clearly an important function of the examination, as is borne out by the usual pass rate of about 75%.

There is a difficulty here in that as the examination may not be taken until the last few weeks of training, and many candidates will have begun to look for partnerships before then, it will often not be possible to indicate 'MRCGP' when applying for partnerships.

16

Why take the examination?

Why take the examination? Because human nature is such that if we know that we are to be examined we will prepare ourselves better than if we are not. We owe it to our patients to be good at our job, and they can rightly ask for evidence that we are. We are also accountable to society which pays our salaries, funds our training and provides the resources we command in carrying out our professional duties.

When is the right time?

When to take the examination? There has been a debate about the best time to take the examination with the greater majority of candidates taking the examination as trainees. However, the new position taken by the College, namely that all future principals in the National Health Service should hold it, has resolved this debate (see Editor's Preface) and all trainees should therefore be advised to take the examination at the end of vocational training.

No doubt there are reasons which could be put forward for not taking the examination. Not to do so, however, is likely to result in a short-sighted and blinkered outlook in a career that lacks the intellectual stimulus which could enhance and illuminate it.

In conclusion, it is interesting to reflect on the words of Dr William Thompson, former Editor of *The Practitioner*. In an editorial welcoming the foundation of the College as "a brave new venture", he said: "An active and progressive College of General Practitioners would safeguard the future of general practice as an integral part of the medical services of this country that offers a satisfying life's work to men [and women] of culture, understanding and integrity" (*Practitioner*, 1953). Forty years on we have good cause to thank those who had the vision and foresight to found the College. To prepare for and pass the MRCGP examination and then contribute to the College as a member will indeed provide much that is satisfying in life's work.

17

References

David J and Prior-Willeard PFS (1993) Resuscitation skills of MRCP candidates. *British Medical Journal* **306**, 1578–9.

General Practice Steering Committee (1953) A College of General Practitioners. Foreword. *Practitioner* **170**, Suppl.

Lowenstein SR, Libby LS, Mountain RD et al. (1981) Cardiopulmonary resuscitation by medical and surgical house officers. *Lancet* **2**, 679–81.

Pai GR, Haites NE and Rawles JM (1987) One thousand heart attacks in Grampian; the place of cardiopulmonary resuscitation in general practice. *British Medical Journal* **294**, 352–4.

Practitioner (1953) College of General Practitioners. Editorial, **170**, 1–2.

Tombleson P and Wakeford R (1989) Why do trainees take the MRCGP Examination? *Journal of the Royal College of General Practitioners* **39**, 168–71.

Vincent R, Martin B, Williams G et al. (1984) A community training scheme for cardiopulmonary resuscitation. *British Medical Journal* **288**, 617–20.

3 The Structure of the Written Papers

The written part of the examination takes place on one day at 12 venues, 10 in the United Kingdom and one each in the Republic of Ireland and Germany (see page 12). It consists of three papers, two of which are of two hours' duration, and one, the critical reading question paper (CRQ), of two and a half hours, extra time being allowed for reading the material presented.

Multiple choice question paper

Most examination candidates will now be familiar with the form of a multiple choice question paper (MCQ), and therefore it need not be described in detail here. In brief, it consists of a series of phrases or 'stems' which introduce a topic, each of which is followed by some statements about that topic. Candidates are invited to say whether they think that the statements are true or false. Correct answers score marks; incorrect ones do not.

Test of factual knowledge

The MCQ paper is the principal test of factual knowledge in the MRCGP examination, and its design is such that little else is tested in it. In the modified essay question paper (MEQ), critical reading paper and in the orals other attributes are tested, and although questions that involve factual knowledge may arise they carry relatively less weight in the generation of marks than they do in the MCQ.

The MCQ is under continuous development, as indeed are the other parts of the examination, in order to improve its reliability and relevance to contemporary medicine. The paper now contains a variable number of stems, each with three to six items relating to it. The total number of items is now approximately 360, and they are designed to cover 15 areas of knowledge required for general practice. The balance of subjects varies from time to time and they are not necessarily grouped together or identified as belonging to a particular group in the question paper.

Marking system

The questions are set out in a booklet (which must be left in the examination hall at the end of the examination), and the answers are given by making marks on a special form designed to be optically read by machine (Appendix 4). Pencils are provided for use in this paper.

The marks are awarded on the 'true/false' basis, that is to say that a correct answer gains one mark, but an incorrect answer or no answer at all gains no marks. Until 1992 there was a 'negative marking' system, but this had the effect of inhibiting candidates who were uncertain of the correct answer, and was found not to discriminate between those who were unsure and therefore avoided giving answers and those whose answers were sometimes right and sometimes wrong and thereby cancelled each other out. It was therefore abandoned in favour of the true/false form. For this reason candidates are advised to attempt as many questions as they can, for nothing will be lost by so doing, and 'intelligent guesses' are very often correct.

Extended matching question

Another development is the introduction from October 1993 of a new form called 'extended matching question'. The purpose here is to test candidates' ability to apply their knowledge to those situations likely to be found in practice and to apply probability in making diagnostic decisions. The questions consist of a series of between three and six clinical situations (called 'items'), set out in two or three sentences each, and a list of possible diagnoses ('options'). The task, which is given in the 'instruction', is to match the most likely diagnostic option to each situation or item. Only one of the diagnostic options may be used for each item. There may be three items in each question, all relating to the same theme, for instance, reduced vision in the eye. Answering this type of question is discussed in Chapter 8. Answers are given on a different form from the usual optically scanned MCQ answer-sheet.

'Trial' questions

As part of the regular development of the MCQ papers some questions (25%) are asked in each examination on a trial basis. These questions do not attract marks for that examination but their validity and reliability are being tested for future use. They will not be distinguishable from the marked questions, and if they are found to be satisfactory they will be included in the bank of questions available for subsequent papers. All questions which are marked and contribute to the totals have actually been tested in this way. If, however, the statistics on the new items indicate that they are unsatisfactory they will not be used. Sometimes they are re-trialled when analysis shows that poor performance is related to lack of recent medical knowledge by the majority of candidates, for instance where recent changes have not yet received widespread acceptance.

Modified essay question paper

Since the very beginning of the MRCGP examination the modified essay question paper (MEQ) has been used and refined as the principal way of assessing candidates' ability in patient management and decision making. Indeed this form of examination was largely developed in the MRCGP. For practical reasons it would be impossible to have enough subjects for a true 'clinical' examination, and in any case much of what is being examined is not simply clinical skill but rather the candidates' understanding of the circumstances in which patients present to doctors and the possible responses to those presentations. The purpose of this part of the examination is therefore to assess candidates' ability to identify the nature of a problem that has been presented to them and to propose a suitable range of solutions. To some extent it also seeks to identify and evaluate their attitudes to the situations described, though this is done in much more detail in the orals, where those attitudes can be discussed, challenged and justified. The MEQ also deals with areas of practice other than the management of clinical problems, such as partnership, legal and ethical matters, and the role of the general practitioner in society.

How it works

In its present form the MEQ is presented as a series of 10 situations which might be encountered in a typical day in general practice. Each situation is described in a few lines at the top of a separate page, the remainder of the page and its reverse being available for the candidate to write the answer. The description is followed by a short question or instruction such as "How might you proceed with this consultation?", or "Outline how you might manage this situation". The answers may be written in the form of notes or statements, as one might set out a synopsis of a fuller answer. It is not expected that candidates will write a full-length essay in grammatically perfect English, but rather that they will set out a list of ideas that come to mind in the situation described and factors which must be considered in order to deal with it satisfactorily.

In earlier years questions tended to follow a single situation as it might develop over time in a practice setting. For instance, there might be a case in which a husband developed heart disease, and the first question would be about the management of that. The next situation might be about the stresses the wife experienced in working to maintain the family income, do the housework and bring up the children. Then there might be the problems encountered as the wife's mother grew old and infirm, followed by the difficulties of adolescent children. With such a format it can seem that such a family has been singled out for grave misfortune, and the scenario loses credibility.

Reliability examined

The MEQ was one of the areas subjected to research and development by the Centre for Medical Education of the University of Dundee (Mulholland, 1988) following Dr David Swanson's careful study of the examination (Swanson, 1985). The Centre demonstrated that the sequential form of question described above might unfairly discriminate against a candidate to whom the situation in the first question was unfamiliar, and that a wider sampling of topics was advisable. The researchers also established that marking of the papers by one examiner was as reliable as by two, and that if 12 or even 14 topics were examined the reliability of the paper would be increased. However, the amount of time available, the stamina of the candidates and the time required for marking demanded a compromise. With the present format the reliability of the MEQ is good with an alpha coefficient of greater than 0.8 (the key test of reliability where 1.0 is ideal and 0.8 or more is acceptable).

As a result of these observations the paper now consists of 10 situations that might occur in everyday practice which are mostly independent of each other, though there might be some relationship between them such as an emergency which makes you late for the next situation and the problems that such a delay might cause. Most of the situations presented concern matters of direct clinical or managerial relevance, for instance about the clinical decisions to be made in a case, or some problem the practice staff have with appointments. However there is sometimes a novel form of question, usually the last one, which is deliberately different in order to avoid the stereotype which can ensue from keeping to a rigid formula, and to introduce variety and originality.

Sitting the paper

Two hours are allowed for the MEQ paper, which is taken during the morning session of the examination day. As there are 10 questions it follows that only 12 minutes are available, on average, to respond to each situation. To some extent this reproduces the sort of time scale that exists in practice.

Answers are therefore expected to contain those ideas which a general practitioner should have at his or her immediate command in actual practice rather than a full and detailed treatise upon the subject. Some topics which have occurred in recent MEQ papers are shown in Table 3.1.

The papers are presented in a stapled leaflet, with one situation and its relevant question at the top of each page. At the end of the day the pages are separated and sent to different examiners for marking, each examiner having to mark one question only. It is important that candidates should know this, for remarks referring to a previous question will not make sense to an examiner who has not seen the other question.

Table 3.1 Some topics in recent MEQ papers

- All aspects of clinical and preventive medicine
- 'Problem' or difficult patients
- Psychological problems in individual patients and families
- The consultation process
- Practice organization
- Relationships with colleagues and others
- Controversial and/or new topics in medicine
- The doctor's own feelings and awareness
- Ethics and attitudes

Critical reading question paper

The critical reading question paper (CRQ) was introduced in 1990 to improve on the old practice topic question paper, which had been shown to be unreliable. The advice of the researchers from the Centre for Medical Education at Dundee was that the paper would need more questions and more examiners, and even then would not be very good. At the same time two other factors were emerging which demanded a new and more relevant form of examination paper. First, the introduction of formal training for general practice and the increasing complexity of the discipline stimulated research, led to the development of clinical and practice management systems, and produced a large body of literature. As medical and management techniques developed in importance and complexity, so accurate and balanced comprehension of the information that was being distributed became more and more important in the everyday work of the general practitioner. Secondly and simultaneously, the pressure for accountability and managerial responsibility from government and society and from within the profession, which culminated in the new contract of 1990, laid stress on quality assurance, efficiency and effectiveness. It was felt by many that this was a potentially threatening development, competing for time and energy with other and arguably more important objectives of medical practice.

The College considered how it might meet the challenge this pressure presented, and its advice included stimulating help for doctors in data collection and analysis, performance review and research as part of the everyday work of their practices (RCGP, 1990). These would be essential skills for future general practitioners.

There arose, therefore, a requirement that aspirants to membership of the College should be able to show their ability to read, analyse and draw conclusions from written material relevant to their work. The flow of printed matter flooding into surgeries demands that general practitioners should be able to abstract the important and the valid but reject the useless quickly, easily and reliably, whether it be in letters, reports, scientific papers, pharmaceutical promotions or government documents. The critical reading paper was developed to test candidates' ability to do this. Some of the topics which have been examined in the critical reading question paper are shown in Table 3.2.

Table 3.2 Some topics in recent CRQ papers

- Topics in Part 1 type questions

  Drugs in the management of chronic asthma
  Recognition of depression
  Methods to help people stop smoking
  Childbirth without consultant obstetricians
  Current thinking on drugs for hypertension

- Material used in Part 2 type questions

  A paper on consultation styles
  A paper on screening for haematuria in men
  Analysis of an audit of night calls
  Data on referral rates in a practice
  A protocol for the care of diabetic patients

Sitting the paper

There were originally three sections in the CRQ paper, but this has now been changed to two, with five parts to each, making 10 questions in all. They must be completed in two and a half hours, which includes some time for reading the material which is presented. All questions must be answered. The first five questions deal with the candidates' familiarity with issues of current interest in general practice, and the last five with their ability to read critically and discriminatingly, using relevant texts or other material presented with the question papers. To score well in this part it is therefore necessary to read the contemporary literature thoroughly when preparing for the examination. The CRQ paper takes place in the afternoon of the examination day.

As in the MEQ, the questions are presented to candidates in the form of a stapled booklet, with one question at the top of each page and space for the answers on both sides of the paper. On completion of the examination the pages are separated and sent to different examiners for marking. It is therefore important to ensure that all answers are written on the relevant page.

Marking the MEQ and CRQ

The MEQ and CRQ papers are distributed to examiners on the day following the examination, and the marking must be completed within two weeks. The marking is done according to schedules constructed at the examiners' annual workshop, which takes place a few weeks before the summer examination, and they are updated or revised if necessary before the autumn diet. At this stage of the examination, examiners are in effect making judgements about the quality of the answers and expressing those judgements numerically in accordance with the prepared schedules. The marks achieved by candidates are then placed in rank order according to their total marks so far, and the mean of all the marks is determined. All candidates whose marks are above the level of one standard deviation below the mean are then invited to attend the oral examination.

It was found that candidates whose written marks were below that level were unable to improve their marks sufficiently at the orals to achieve an overall pass mark, and therefore it would be of no value to them to attend and would be an unfruitful use of their time and the examination's resources. However, it is permissible to enter the examination again, although in such cases it is advisable that advice is taken about suitable training and preparation.

References

Mulholland H (1988) Report to the Examination Board, RCGP. Unpublished.

Royal College of General Practitioners (1990) An educational strategy for general practice for the 1990s. In *A College Plan—Priorities for the Future. Occasional Paper 49.* London, RCGP.

Swanson DB (1985) Report to the Examination Board, RCGP. Unpublished.

4 The Oral Examination

Candidates who are successful in the written part of the examination are invited to attend the orals, which take place at the Royal College of Physicians in Edinburgh and the Royal College of General Practitioners in London, about six weeks later. In practice about 85% of candidates gain enough marks to go to the orals. Those who feel that they may not have done as well as they would have liked in the papers and whose marks are below the eventual pass mark at this stage have an opportunity in the orals to create a good impression at personal interview. They can and often do pass the examination overall. However, experience has shown that those who score very low marks in the papers do not improve their scores enough at the orals to pass the full examination, and are therefore not invited to attend.

Although provisional notification of the date of their orals is given to candidates at the time of their written examination, confirmation is sent when the written results are known, usually about four weeks after the date of the papers. Before then, however, the practice experience questionnaire (PEQ) must be completed and sent to the Examination Department, as this forms the basis of questions in the first oral.

Practice experience questionnaire

When the MRCGP examination was introduced in 1965 it was clear that an assessment of candidates' ability in day-to-day activities should be made. This would include not only clinical and communication skills but also the way in which the candidates' practices were organized and managed. Direct assessment by observation of clinical examination and decision making is still a difficulty, although this may be overcome by various means such as videorecording of real consultations, simulated surgeries or objective structured clinical examination (OSCE), which will be considered in Chapter 15.

The College's practicable alternative to this was the 'log diary', by which information was sought about the candidate's practice and a list of cases the candidate had seen. Though this form served well in the early years, it became clear that it was not meeting the needs of an examination which was increasingly being taken by candidates who were completing their training and therefore not responsible for the practices they were describing. This, together with the rapid changes in general practice, demanded that the formula be updated. Thus in 1990 the log diary passed into the sunset to be replaced by the newly formulated practice experience questionnaire. It must be said, however, that old ideas die hard and the name of 'log diary' is still used by some who find change difficult!

Unlike the change from the 'essay' paper to the CRQ this change was not revolutionary, for the purpose remains the same, namely to show the examiners the circumstances in which the candidate has been working, and a sample of cases that have been managed. A realistic appraisal of the candidate's approach can then be made, using the candidate's own experience as the starting point.

It is important to understand that the information given in the questionnaire itself is not marked, nor is the practice which it describes being examined. It is what the candidate says in the oral examination in relation to that information which generates marks.

The PEQ is intended primarily as a tool for the examination but as in all examinations the selection of subjects to be tested may influence the preparation, so the need to complete the PEQ may draw attention to aspects of practice which the candidate might otherwise overlook. This is particularly likely in situations where trainees, though taking a full part in the clinical work of the practice, are nevertheless supernumary and may not become involved in long-term decisions about practice management or development. It thus has an educational spin-off which it is hoped will benefit candidates' preparation for practice. Such a spin-off need not be confined to those preparing for the examination, for practitioners, whether trainers or not, might well use the questionnaire as a basis for a searching look at themselves.

The questionnaire consists of six parts, as shown in Table 4.1 and the whole form is reproduced in Appendix 5. The way in which the questionnaire is used will be discussed in more detail in Chapter 11.

Table 4.1 Information sought in the practice experience questionnaire

- Candidate's identification and status
- Practice structure
- Practice organization and facilities
- Workload
- The candidate's own ideas and experience
- List of cases managed in surgeries, on visits, and in emergency

---

Sitting the orals

The two oral examinations are of half an hour duration each, with a few minutes' interval between them to allow for marking and re-organization. Each is conducted by two examiners, but the candidate returns to a different pair for the second oral, so in effect is assessed by four examiners. The tables at which the orals take place are mostly arranged in large rooms with up to 10 tables in each, and screened from each other to some extent to prevent distraction.

Observers

In addition to the two examiners the candidate may also find an 'observer', who takes no part in the examination process and should be (and always is) ignored. Observers are usually other examiners who, by watching their colleagues, can broaden their own experience and also make constructive criticism of the examination process and thus develop consistency. Occasionally the observer is a visitor from another college, another examination authority, or from another country, who may be interested in the nature of the MRCGP examination system. All observers meet after their period of observation to discuss what they have seen in a critical and developmental way.

Use of videotape

Occasionally a candidate may find that a closed-circuit television camera is present but need have no anxiety about this. It is focused on the examiners, and although all voices are recorded, the videotape is used only to assess the examination process and the examiners' techniques. It has no function in the examination itself, nor in the awarding of marks. It is, however, an important part of the continuing training and improvement of examiners' methods. From time to time all examiners have a period of re-assessment using the videotapes in group discussion with their colleagues in order to improve their skills and gain insight by seeing themselves in action.

A test of attitudes

In the early years of the MRCGP examination the orals simply provided an opportunity to test candidates in clinical problems and to challenge them a little more than could be done in the papers. However, this lacked consistency and structure and it became necessary to develop the process further to ensure reliability and validity, and in order to discriminate between the good and the very good as well as the not so good. Whereas factual knowledge is best tested in the MCQ and the application of that knowledge in the MEQ, the orals are the only place where candidates can be tested about their attitudes, and can be challenged to say how and why they developed and hold them.

Under the guidance of Dr David Pendleton, then Psychological Adviser to the Examination Board, the examiners compiled a long list of attributes which they were seeking at the orals. On analysis these were found to fall into seven distinct groups, called 'areas of competence', shown here in Table 4.2 and discussed in detail in Chapter 11. It will be noted that the headings are not all essentially clinical, which at first may seem surprising in a medical

31

Table 4.2 The seven areas of competence in the oral
examination

- Problem definition

- Management

- Prevention

- Practice organization

- Communication

- Professional values

- Personal and professional growth

---

examination. A heading such as 'Organization' for instance, could be found in an examination on banking or engineering. What is being tested in this area is actually the candidates' ability to organize their efforts and resources in a medical or clinical field. It is not pure knowledge that is being assessed, or 'correct' answers being sought, but evidence of how well knowledge is applied, how decisions are made and resources prioritized, how relative values such as cost and kindness are assessed, and how well candidates understand the reasons for and implications of doing what they propose in their answers. Of course knowledge is important, even though it is not the primary reason for awarding marks; a candidate who is evidently ignorant will not do well and the candidate who is very well informed may enhance his or her marks. Given that the knowledge base is secure, however, good marks will be gained by those who can show the following attributes:

- That they have a range of reasonable alternative responses to a given situation

- That they understand the implications of the actions they have taken or advised

- That the reasons given for their actions are well argued and supported by evidence where possible

- That they can be flexible in their attitudes where appropriate

- That their behaviour is consistent with their expressed attitudes.

Areas of competence

In each part of the oral examination the examiners will attempt to cover most or all of the seven areas of competence, but as time is limited usually five or six are completed. To cover more would mean that they were examined too superficially to be sure of the candidate's competence; to cover less might not be representative and therefore the conclusions might be invalid. It is often the case that a topic might fall into more than one area, and to some extent allocation of the area is arbitrary, but the intention is to ensure that as many areas of practice as possible are examined at each oral.

The first pair of examiners note the topics discussed on a special form, which is then passed to the second pair, and in this way duplication of topics is avoided. However, each pair must cover the seven areas of competence as far as they can. A candidate may therefore be asked to discuss the same area in both orals but, if 'Prevention' were the area for example, in the first oral this might relate to something in the questionnaire, such as a travel immunization clinic, and in the second to management of smoking and hypercholesterolaemia in the prevention of coronary heart disease.

The questions

Whereas the questions in the written part of the examination are compiled by a group of examiners and marked according to schedules prepared in advance, those in the orals are devised by the examiners individually, either in advance or spontaneously as the examination proceeds. They may be chosen from any area relevant to general practice.

In the first oral questions are based on the questionnaire, which the examiners will have read in advance. Usually about half the time is spent in discussing issues relating to the practice described, and the other half is used to address matters arising from the list of cases, although this varies from one examiner pair to another, and according to the content of the questionnaire. Clearly it is not possible to award marks for answers which the examiners cannot corroborate, so often the questions are phrased in general terms about issues raised, rather than about the cases themselves. Thus it might be that the question is not "What did you do?", which is unmarkable because the examiner was not a witness, but rather "Why did you do that?" or "What other options were there?", both of which will explore the candidate's thinking. Candidates should not therefore be disappointed if their carefully prepared cases do not provide them with the opportunity to demonstrate their clinical acumen in interesting situations.

In the second oral the questions are based on material prepared in advance, and they are refined and sharpened by repeated use and the constructive criticism of fellow examiners, either as co-examiners or observers, or as a result of the group discussions of orals that have been videorecorded. They usually arise out of cases which the examiners have experienced themselves and which have posed a clinical or ethical dilemma, or from issues raised by recent developments of professional, ethical or social matters. Areas of medicopolitical interest or moral uncertainty may be raised, not because the 'politically correct' answer is required but to discover whether the candidate has considered his or her position in that respect, and how and why he or she might react if that situation were to present itself in real life. An example of the first kind of question might arise from a situation in which a patient complained of abdominal pain thought to be due to alcoholic gastritis but who denied that he drank to excess; examples of the second might be the cost-benefit, and social and clinical implications of mammography screening, or the effect of poverty, unemployment and housing on health.

Usually the examination of a particular topic will start with a general question about the area the examiner wishes to cover, and will then proceed to more detailed or thorough probing to discover the extent of the candidate's competence. It is not knowledge but understanding which is being tested, and the examiner is intentionally exposing the conflicts and paradoxes inherent in many medical issues. Awareness of and the ability to respond to the needs of the patient, the feelings of the doctor, and the expectations of society are all valid qualities in a general practitioner and are involved in the resolution of those conflicts and paradoxes. The successful candidate will be one who can discuss these matters in the light of knowledge based on evidence which can be quoted and who can state his or her view with confidence and insight.

Marking the orals

Having covered as many of the areas of competence as possible in the time available, the examiners have to award an overall mark for that oral. They award their marks individually without conferring and do not need to agree.

Each question is given a mark as the examination proceeds, and at the end each examiner makes a final judgement according to a scale in which the possible marks, indicated by a single letter rather than a number, are described verbally. Thus the very best that can be obtained is 'Outstanding', which is described as "a very rare candidate, uniformly outstanding. Well read, coherent, critical ... etc". Then come descriptions summarized as 'Excellent', 'Good' ("well informed ... good decision-making skills") and 'Satisfactory'. The category 'Satisfactory' deems the candidate to have "... a reassuring solidness ...", and that he or she is "able to justify only some approaches well, but most appear sensible". Such a candidate has adequate but not good decision-making skills. 'Bare pass' is just on the borderline, which means that a candidate who has marks at or above the mean in the papers will probably pass, but not if the papers are poor.

Below 'Bare pass' are 'Not very good' and 'Unsatisfactory', which describe the candidate who has inconsistent and unjustifiable approaches, and 'Poor', which means the examiners think the candidate is so incoherent as to be unpassable. Finally comes 'Dangerous'.

Fortunately 'Dangerous' is a mark that is very rarely used, but it does raise an important point. There might be a candidate who seemed for some reason to be acting in an entirely irresponsible way, and the examiners would therefore have to decide whether to act upon that evidence as would any colleague of such a doctor. They can, if necessary, make a note on the marking sheet to the effect that a candidate appears to be dangerous in some respect, so that the Examination Board can act appropriately. Clearly it would be entirely wrong to admit to the College someone who was capable of gaining enough marks to pass the examination but was acting illegally or dangerously. However, such a procedure has rarely been used and not at all in the last two years, and exists only to meet the need should it arise, however improbable that might be.

The final marks

The marks given by each examiner are now added to the marks gained in the papers, and a total is calculated on computer. It is so arranged that the marks are divided equally between the five sections of the examination, each section of the written part and each oral contributing one fifth of the total. Any candidate who achieves an aggregate of 50% overall will pass. Although it is not intended to have a fixed proportion of successes, it is usual for about 75% of candidates to pass at each diet of the examination.

Fraser Rose Medal

Those candidates whose marks are within the top 2.5% of those gained by all candidates who sit the written examination are awarded a distinction, and this is noted in the published pass list. The highest accolade, the Fraser Rose Medal, is awarded to the candidate who achieves the most marks in each academic year. This honour is presented to the recipient at the College's Annual General Meeting each year. Until now (1993) 22 Fraser Rose Medals have been awarded, including two presented in 1986/7, when the same high mark was achieved by two candidates.

In the past there was a procedure by which the performance of candidates whose marks fell just below the pass mark could be reviewed by the four oral examiners, a system known for obvious reasons as a 'quartet'. This no longer operates because of a change in the marking system intended to distribute the proportion of marks evenly between the five parts of the whole examination, which delays the final calculation of the marks until after the end of the orals, by which time the examiners are no longer available to confer.

The pass list

As soon as the whole examination ends the pass list is compiled and the results are published within one day of the end of the orals, being mailed to all candidates and placed on the notice-board in the College. For reasons of accuracy and to avoid confusion no information about results is given on the telephone.

It is, of course, unfortunate for candidates who are not successful but they should be encouraged to attempt the examination again, for the College wishes to make itself available to all who strive to achieve its standards and uphold its objectives. Those who do not pass are invited to write to the Examination Department to obtain some feedback on where they could improve their performance. One of the incidental tasks of examiners in the orals is to make a brief note of their overall impression of the candidate's performance where this might be useful. Such information, together with the marks obtained in each section, is then relayed to any candidate who asks for it, and where appropriate some guidance is given about what might be done to improve performance in future.

Those who are successful may congratulate themselves on a well deserved achievement and look forward to the benefits of membership of their Royal College. They can also take satisfaction in having laid the foundations of an education on which they can build further as they proceed through their careers.

5 Strategies for Preparation, Part 1

Whatever the reason individual candidates may have for taking the examination, its purpose is to decide whether the candidate has attained a standard of skill, competence and experience that justifies membership of the Royal College of General Practitioners. This begs the question "What is general practice?" and this must be answered in order to determine what skills, competence and experience are relevant to the work, and therefore the examination.

Job description

The foundations of the educational process for general practice were laid in 1969 when a working party, set up by the College under the chairmanship of Dr John Horder, agreed and published a job definition of the general practitioner. It gave its full recommendations in *The Future General Practitioner—Learning and Teaching* (RCGP, 1972). More than twenty years have passed since the report was published but its recommendations are still valid, which shows how accurate its predictions were. It has been and still is a secure foundation for education for general practice.

The Future General Practitioner begins with a job description, which all aspiring general practitioners would do well to study. It defines the general practitioner as "… a doctor who provides personal, primary and continuing care to individuals and families", and goes on to say: "He may attend his patients in their own homes, in his consulting room or sometimes in hospital. He accepts responsibility for making an initial decision on every problem his patient may present to him, consulting with specialists when appropriate…" It states that even though single-handed the general practitioner is part of a team and will sometimes need to delegate; also that: "His diagnoses will be composed in physical, psychological and social terms. He will intervene educationally, preventively and therapeutically to promote his patient's health." Perhaps the only omission which is significant, and all too apparent with the wisdom of hindsight, is the very important contribution that women doctors make, not only to the care of patients but to the collective quality and wisdom of partnerships and the profession as a whole.

This job description puts responsibility on general practitioners in several important areas:

- In the patients' own homes ... not just 'the community', but where they actually live

- For the initial decision on every problem, which may be in emergency or in other critical situations

- For teamwork as well as individual relationships with patients

- For education of patients

- For prevention as well as treatment of disease

- For consideration of social factors in the health of patients.

Eleven goals

The Future General Practitioner goes on to consider 11 goals in education for general practice, which arise from the job description and which are summarized in Table 5.1. It also lists five areas of learning on which the examination for membership should be based, shown in Table 5.2. Although these are the basis of a curriculum for study, there is no detailed syllabus published by the College or the Examination Board, neither does the College itself prescribe policies which it requires its members to accept. The Panel of Examiners, to whom responsibility is delegated by Council, devises the examination within those five areas and, taking account of recent developments and research, responds to the changes in practice as they occur. Attention to these goals and the areas within them would therefore be an appropriate way of developing a strategy for preparation, and act as a framework which

39

candidates can use to direct their studies. The reader is encouraged to refer to the original work (the goals are set out in Chapter 1).

Table 5.1 The goals of the general practitioner

1 Make diagnoses expressed simultaneously in physical, psychological and social terms

2 Recognize that the patient is a unique individual

3 Make decisions about every problem presented

4 Understand and use time appropriately

5 Understand how interpersonal relationships in families can affect health and influence illness

6 Understand how social factors influence health and illness

7 Show a range of options for intervention

8 Manage a practice properly

9 Recognize the need for continuing education

10 Understand research as related to general practice

11 Audit his or her own work critically

Table 5.2 The content of the examination

- Clinical practice—Health and disease

- Clinical practice—Human development

- Clinical practice—Human behaviour

- Medicine and society

- The practice

Many of these goals also apply to other areas of medical practice which overlap with primary care, and indeed to professions allied to medicine. They describe very well the foundations on which good practice is built, and thereby provide a curriculum which the candidate for the MRCGP should cover, for these are the areas of competence in which the candidate will be examined.

Taken in more detail, goals 1 and 2 require that general practitioners must know what is normal in their patient's society, and how that may differ from place to place or for cultural or ethnic reasons; they must know what stresses and supports exist therein and what are the effects of deviation from the accepted norms. The patient, however, is unique and care must be modified accordingly and appropriately to that individual. Goal 3 emphasizes the 'generalness' of the general practitioner, and that patients may, and often do, present a great variety of problems, whether typically medical or not. These problems must be recognized, considered and managed, but not necessarily by the general practitioner alone.

General practice is a long-term commitment (Goal 4) and the duration of relationships between the doctor and the patient may vary from the immediate to the lifelong. Time is also a valuable resource which may be used effectively in a variety of ways and is an important factor in both clinical and practice management. It can be wasted by inefficiency and poor management and such waste can be costly to doctors and their staff, as well as to patients and others. If used wisely it can promote activity that is beneficial, and time used in planning and effective action can save time that might otherwise be squandered.

General practitioners must understand how health and illness are influenced by the environment, by the relationships within families and by society, which is encapsulated in the phrase 'family doctor' (Goals 5 and 6). Factors such as the health of other family members, the relationships between parents and children, husband and wife, employer and employee, or between workmates; influences such as poverty and deprivation, unemployment, industrial and working conditions, environmental pollution, noise and congestion all affect health. The doctor can sometimes change things for the better (or worse) through intervention, sometimes not, but it is always important to recognize these influences and their effects where they exist, for not to do so is to risk inappropriate action. This is no new discovery, for John Donne said it succinctly: "No man is an island, entire of itself; every man is a piece of the Continent, a part of the main."

In Goal 7 the general practitioner is revealed again as the generalist. Interventions are not just therapeutic or pharmacological but may be educational, explanatory, supportive, or psychotherapeutic; or they may consist of referral to some other agency, which need not be medical. The present emphasis on physical exercise and a healthy diet, and on the avoidance of, or compensation for, both physical and emotional stress are good examples of this approach.

Goal 8 makes the point that to be successful and competent the self-employed doctor must also manage a business, which nowadays may involve an investment of hundreds of thousands or even millions of pounds, and an annual turnover of the same magnitude. This necessitates the employment of staff, often in large numbers and of various disciplines, and awareness of employers' legal responsibilities in that respect. There may also be other members of the primary care team towards whom the doctor has responsibilities though not employing them directly. Moreover there is the responsibility of using public resources wisely and cost-effectively, in such areas as referrals to hospital and the management of fundholding practices or contribution to commissioning systems. To do this well the general practitioner needs skills that are not taught in the ordinary medical curriculum and must be learnt elsewhere, preferably not by painful experience.

Finally, and by no means least important, Goals 9, 10 and 11 discuss the educational needs of the doctor and of the support staff for whom the doctor is responsible, saying that such education must be based on published research and continuing observation of practice. The doctor need not necessarily do the research but must understand its method and implications. Observation of practice, that is to say audit, is necessary to show whether what should be done (which is determined by research) is actually being done as intended, and if not, where it needs to be changed or improved. General practitioners have a responsibility to their patients and to the taxpayer who funds the resources of the

National Health Service to be as effective and as efficient as they can, so they must know how well they are doing and be prepared to change and adapt if necessary.

Knowledge, skills and attitudes

This, then, is the range of matters that constitute the general practitioner's work and responsibilities, and therefore is the basis on which the MRCGP examination is devised. There is, however, another way of analysing an educational syllabus, namely the familiar triad of knowledge, skills and attitudes. It is not sufficient, for instance, merely to know that interpersonal relationships can affect health. A doctor might be able to describe the cause and effect of a family dispute with great clarity yet lack the skill to intervene effectively. Or another might have a detailed knowledge of how smoking causes disease but not understand the role of the general practitioner in the prevention of those diseases. And however moved a doctor might be by a patient's condition, it is necessary to have the relevant knowledge and skill to diagnose and manage that condition appropriately.

Candidates preparing for the MRCGP must therefore cover a lot of ground, much of which is not purely medical. They should look outside the factual, scientific or practical aspects of their work to areas of personal, social and environmental relevance, for these, too, contain things which cause the problems that patients bring to us their doctors. As well as asking: "What do I know about respiratory disease?" or "Can I list all the signs of alcohol abuse?", the candidate should also be able to ask and answer questions like "How good am I at teaching patients about the effects of smoking?" and "Is this family's unhappiness caused by someone's problem with alcohol?". A stereotyped and rigid approach to practice based only on textbook knowledge, where facts are known but skill, insight and understanding are lacking, gains few marks in the MRCGP examination—just as it lacks success in the real world. Knowledge is important, but so too are the ability to assess all the relevant factors in a case, to present a range of possibilities for its management, and to understand their implications.

Sources of learning

How, then, can the aspiring member of the College acquire all the knowledge, develop the skills and adopt the appropriate attitudes that professional competence demands? The sources are many, none of them complete in themselves, but each is part of a mosaic which, taken together with the other parts, forms the complete picture. The sources described here are not necessarily complete, for the effective and competent general practitioner uses all the features of personality that make up a mature person. Table 5.3 shows a summary of the more important sources of learning.

Table 5.3 Some sources of learning in preparation for general practice

- Experience
- Learned journals
- Medical newspapers and periodicals
- Seminars and group work
- Projects and research
- Audit of own or others' work
- Own personality, interests and attitude to life
- Textbooks
- Journal clubs
- Distance learning packages
- Courses
- Tutorials
- Informal peer discussions

Experience is put at the top of the list because if used well it can teach maturity and wisdom, and is, moreover, a principal source of learning and adaptation by adults. It can only do so, however, when a self-questioning approach has been adopted. Such an approach recognizes success, asks why and how it has occurred, and is prepared to acknowledge failure and ask the same questions. No one is perfect, certainly not the beginner in a complex and skilled profession, and it should not be seen as a sign of weakness that mistakes and deficiencies occur; rather, the ability to learn from mistakes should be seen as a strength. Although at the bottom of the list, personality, interest and attitude to life are every bit as important, and their place at the bottom betokens the fact that they are fundamental to success in the profession.

Textbooks

Perhaps little needs to be said about the place of textbooks, for they are familiar to all and contain the information necessary for proper diagnosis, investigation and treatment of the conditions likely to be encountered. There is, too, a wide range of books on matters such as consultation skills, communication, practice management and finance, audit and research, and ethics and law: indeed the whole range of practice activity. They must be the most reliable source of consensus information available in a convenient and collected form.

However, much of what takes place in general practice and which the candidate needs to study is experiential, that is to say it concerns the interaction between doctor and patient both inside and outside the consulting room, as well as all the other interactions which go on in the practice of medicine, such as with staff, colleagues and other professionals. It is not enough merely to have a detailed knowledge of the standard clinical textbooks: it is necessary to learn how and when to use or to refrain from using the information they contain, and that must be learned in other ways, discussed below. However, given that textbooks are essential they should be read widely; the reader should think critically about the contents and discuss them freely with colleagues and others.

Learned journals

Learned journals are the principal source of up-to-date information on research, developments and current thinking. They must therefore form the core of preparation for the examination, especially for the CRQ, which is specifically designed to test candidates' competence in this area. However, the sheer volume of new papers on all manner of subjects may defeat even the most avid reader, and it is essential to have a system, and to be selective. The *British Journal of General Practice* and the *British Medical Journal* are the principal vehicles of information about new developments in general practice. There are many others, notably *Family Medicine*, which introduces an international aspect to the literature of primary care and in this way broadens the outlook beyond the administrative and political confines of the National Health Service, where most British general practice is carried on. It is important, too, to read the medical newspapers, for they cover a large range of topics which would take the reader much time to discover in any other way, thereby enhancing awareness of important issues. However, they are not always the impartial and dispassionate sources of information that are needed for education, and reliance on them for important learning should be tempered with caution.

Reading is a solitary occupation, but no one can practise medicine in isolation. The need to communicate ideas and information between colleagues and fellow professionals is paramount—as is the need to communicate with patients. For this reason the exchange of information by word of mouth is a vital part of the preparation for general practice; not only does it deal with the declared subject-matter but it exemplifies and develops that form of communication which doctors most often use with patients. The expression of thoughts and the conveyance of information are tools of the trade, needing well chosen words with clear meaning, so doctors must learn to use them well and keep them in good order. Whether the learning is in the one-to-one situation of a tutorial, the broader setting of a small group, or a task-orientated project, the essence of this form of education is the development of the ability to understand another person's thinking and to respond to it appropriately.

Tutorials

One of the requirements of a training practice is that the trainee should have a period of time each week in one-to-one teaching. On the face of it this clearly provides the supervision that any inexperienced worker needs to learn the job, but there is more to it than simply overseeing the newcomer's work. The beginner in general practice, however experienced in some areas, may be surprised by the breadth of the activities required, and needs to go through the whole gamut of general practice skills to reveal his or her strengths and weaknesses. Unless this is recognized at an early stage, there may be areas which are left uncovered because they are not recognized, or are left too late to correct.

The tutorial is also a time when problems that occur in daily practice can be discussed in confidence and with a thoroughness that might not be possible under the pressure of the day's work. Who has never had a problem that needs thought and consideration to resolve, or needs to be considered in the light of someone else's greater experience? Anyone learning a profession as complex as general practice needs a mentor, that is to say a person with whom ideas can be discussed, exchanged, developed or rejected, who can make the learner feel good and his or her efforts worthwhile, and offer support and encouragement when the going is difficult.

Finally, the tutorial provides an opportunity for counselling, where personal or emotional experience can be explored, difficulties discussed and ideas for resolving them developed. Like the consultation between patient and doctor, the tutorial should be a relationship comprising a meeting of two people each of whom has knowledge, skills and attitudes, as well as needs, and in which appropriate exchange can occur. Whether these qualities are covert or overt, and though they may be held to a different degree by the two people, their exchange and interaction leads to development and growth.

There are limitations to the tutorial, however, because the individual tutor cannot be omniscient. The teaching will necessarily be limited by the competence and outlook of the tutor, the extent of his knowledge and interests, and the time and enthusiasms available to both teacher and pupil. In any case, adults learn by experience and reflection as well as by 'tuition', so it is necessary for the learner to have other systems by which that experience and the reflection upon it may be fostered.

Small groups

Although doctors act most often as individuals in relationships with patients and others, they belong at different times to various groups, which include colleagues and practice staff, patients and their relatives, committees and councils, and many other gatherings that make up society as a whole. Learning to be a general practitioner must therefore include learning how to fit into the microcosms of practice and the neighbourhood, and the small group is an excellent way of doing this. This form of learning is particularly effective in developing self-awareness and the ability to understand relationships. Many of the vocational training courses for general practice include such learning-orientated group work.

Groups may be structured in a variety of ways. Commonly they deal with case presentations selected either randomly or according to some plan. In such a situation a doctor learns to present the essential features of a case, to think of alternatives that may exist in its diagnosis and management, and to justify the decisions made or proposed. Other members of the group may have different ideas about it, and the debates that follow develop the group's skills in thinking rationally about those ideas and their implications. Thus not only are the skills of preparation, oral presentation and discussion rehearsed, but each member of the group gains from the experience and knowledge of the others.

There is more to small groups than the exchange of ideas, the sharing of knowledge and the solving of each other's practical problems. A well run small group will develop an identity of its own, with its own emotional bonds and tensions. In this environment it is possible to learn much about oneself and the way in which one responds to other people and to challenges and difficulties. One can share other people's pleasures and pains, thereby learning about one's own behaviour in similar situations. Using the group as a model with polyvalent responses, it is possible to learn how our patients feel about their problems and how we respond to them with our own feelings. This is vital in a general practitioner, for whether we like it or not, we deal in an area of feeling. If we were to isolate ourselves from our feelings and those we are there to help, we would lose our ability to care; but if we can recognize and understand our own feelings we can learn not only to tolerate them but to use them when appropriate in a helpful and constructive way.

Perhaps the most sophisticated form of small group for doctors is the Balint group, in which the whole interaction between the doctor and the patient, as well as the personal feelings and experiences of the group members, are examined. The contribution made by Balint to the study of the doctor–patient relationship is fundamental to general practice as it has developed in the United Kingdom. Though perhaps too prolonged for the timescale of the trainee year, it is an experience which anyone entering general practice would do well to seek. The Balint group is an ideal form of mentor for the candidate who is already in practice and therefore does not have any other formal tutor during the time of preparation.

As with the tutorial, the small group has its limitations too. For instance there is no syllabus, so many areas of practice may escape inclusion. Because it is based on the knowledge and experience of its members it may lack the resources to deal with matters of fact or reality. It may be taken over by the demands of some of its members to the exclusion of the needs of others, and may founder for the want of good leadership. Indeed small groups are not without their difficulties and dangers. Because they deal in the currency of emotion as well as fact, issues and problems may arise which individuals might prefer to ignore or suppress. Therefore the leader of the group must be skilled in this field and able to handle difficulties that arise. With that safeguard there should be no fear of injury but rather an opportunity for increased self-awareness and personal growth, thereby preventing harm from similar situations in real life that might be even more destructive. It is a great skill to create an effective group in which learning and growth can occur, and though something may happen when seven or eight people form such a group, it is not always as constructive as everyone would wish unless the leader is competent.

Courses

There can be no doubt that a course with a specific objective is an excellent method of teaching. By bringing together experts in a particular field, using sophisticated audiovisual and other methods now available, and by structuring the course appropriately, it is possible to provide opportunities for learning that cannot be provided otherwise. For imparting facts, describing principles or techniques, and for disseminating new ideas or information to many people at the same time there is no better way. The quality of the course depends on the organizers, the teachers and the methods of presentation, as well as the environment. Attendance at a course may open up new fields of interest or excitement for the learner, who can then develop new-found enthusiasm by reading or further study and practice. The opportunity to do something practical in a 'hands-on' way, as for instance in acupuncture or manipulation, often cannot be obtained by any other method, and there is also the opportunity for questions and discussion with the experts or other course members to develop deeper understanding.

Courses are time-consuming, however, particularly in that they often interrupt the working routine, and must therefore be chosen with care according to individual need and interests. It would be easy to become a full-time course-goer to the exclusion of seeing patients, and that would not guarantee success in any examination! Furthermore, mere attendance at a course does not necessarily ensure learning; many a course member has fallen asleep as the after-lunch speaker drones on monotonously in a darkened room. Motivation is necessary to maintain attention, and that comes from a thoughtful choice of courses to attend, based on individual needs, discussed with tutors if appropriate, revealed by experience and discovered by discussion with others in the same situation.

Learning from experience

How easy it is to be wise after the event! The 'retrospectoscope' is perhaps the most effective diagnostic medical instrument in medical practice, at least as far as learning from experience goes. If used properly it can show us where we have been successful, where we could have done differently and where we have failed. When the instrument indicates success we can justly be pleased with ourselves, and as nothing succeeds like success it will reinforce that pattern of behaviour to ensure that it happens again. But when it shows a result less satisfactory than we would like, using the retrospectoscope becomes the one medical technique which hurts the doctor more than the patient. Therein lies the value of thinking about what we have done, why we did it, and how we can learn to do it better. It is not enough just to stumble on, hoping that we will learn a few useful lessons in the great school of life. There needs to be a determination to learn, an attitude of mind in which one develops the habit of observing oneself at work. Such an attitude requires that questions be asked all the time, such as: "Why do this ...?" and "How is that done . . ?" and "What did I do well (or badly) in this or that case?".

The habit of self-observation and self-criticism is good but may not be enough by itself; it needs structure and support. The structure may be obtained by keeping a diary in which a note is made of relevant experience, and of areas where further experience is required. Thus there could be headings under which to record the names of patients who have been seen and about whom subsequent consideration would be useful, for instance by reading the relevant books or papers. There could be records of cases of cancer and terminal care, or of hospital admissions, pregnancies, night calls or emergencies. It should not only record the unusual or outstanding cases but also the common presentations which make up the everyday work of practice. This will ensure that a proper perspective is obtained on the work that has been done, and provide an opportunity to see what else there may be to do. It is not unusual for a trainee to approach the end of a year in practice and discover that some vital area, such as various emergency situations, the follow-up of bereaved relatives, or the arrangement of admission to hospital under the Mental Health Act has not been experienced. While it may not be possible to arrange the necessary procedure in reality, with a diary of experience the missing areas can be identified and studied as required. Having identified the experience gained and still needed, the diary can be used as a basis for activities in the various learning situations described above. It can be used to provide material for case discussions, in tutorials or small groups, and to guide the basic reading and study.

Peer support

There is another source of support whose value should not be underestimated, and that is one's peers. Whether this support is gained informally during the coffee-break, a game of golf or a Sunday stroll, or more formally in practice meetings or young practitioners' groups, the knowledge that there are others facing the same challenges and difficulties is reassuring and supportive. General practice is conducted in the isolation and privacy of the consultation or sick room, is constrained by the needs of confidentiality, and deals in the fields of emotion and feelings, often very negative ones. No practitioner can distance himself from this without loss of effectiveness, and therefore needs to have some means of relieving the pressures that it generates. Sympathetic colleagues can help the newcomer to share in the collective wisdom of the profession, thereby lightening the load of stress and anxiety.

No doctor, young or old, should be afraid to express the worries or the pleasures of work with colleagues; and colleagues should always be ready to respond to such expressions.

An essential skill

The methods of learning outlined above all deal with communication in one way or another. Communication is an essential skill in general practice, and assessment of candidates' ability in this area is an important part of the MRCGP examination. Attention to this part of the learning process, as well as to the subject matter, will pay good dividends when answering in the examination.

References

Donne J (1571–1631) *Devotions upon Emergent Occasions. XVII.* Oxford, OUP.

Royal College of General Practitioners (1972) *The Future General Practitioner—Learning and Teaching.* London, British Medical Journal.

6 Strategies for Preparation, Part 2

The methods of preparation discussed in the previous chapter have been subject-orientated or have touched upon specific methods or systems. All are directed at creating an attitude of mind which is self-critical and questioning in a positive and constructive way. It is worth emphasizing that the MRCGP is not merely a test of knowledge but a higher professional examination which assesses the ability of a professional person to use knowledge responsibly.

A professional approach

The *Shorter Oxford English Dictionary* defines a profession as "a vocation which one professes to be skilled in or to follow" and a skill as "that which is reasonable, proper, right or just". Anyone who seeks to demonstrate his or her suitability to enter the higher levels of a profession must be able to give reasons for a given behaviour and show why it is right or proper in the circumstances. Justice, in the sense of fairness and relevance as well as in conformity with the law, is also a part of professionalism. All these areas are on the agenda for the examination and must therefore be addressed in preparation for it.

It may be good to accept the collective wisdom of our peers and predecessors, and of course, we must take seriously the knowledge and skills developed by others through experience and research. However, the development of an effective and caring system of practice appropriate to local needs requires that we should also question the methods we use ourselves and the attitudes we hold. For instance, we might ask ourselves such questions as:

- Am I doing this procedure as it should be done?

- Am I getting the results I should expect?

- Is this system as efficient as it could be?

- Is it the most suitable system in the circumstances?

- What do my patients think about it?

Indeed it has been said that if one is never dissatisfied one will never make progress. Asking such questions therefore is the first step to progress, but if one is to obtain useful answers from which learning can ensue some structure is required. One such structure is to undertake a specific project, with a view to making a comprehensive study of a particular aspect of practice or even developing a service or system where none existed before. Another is to carry out audit of one's own work or that of others, and this may be done alone or collaboratively. These methods have value not only in preparation for the examination but in the development of general professional ability, both clinical and managerial. A third method is research, but as a method of preparation for a general examination it is probably too specific in its orientation, though that is not to suggest that it is inappropriate for general practitioners to carry out research activities.

Projects

A project in the educational sense is an orderly investigation or study of a specific subject, which may simply be exploratory, or may have some predetermined purpose or intended outcome. In the former case it only describes the condition under study and may go no further unless that condition is so unsatisfactory as to demand a remedy, which then forms a new project. If there is some predetermined purpose there will be an element of change as the purpose is implemented, and the introduction of change is therefore one of the benefits of the exercise.

Management of change

The management of change is an important aspect of the responsibilities of practice and the skills required for it must be studied and learned along with so many other skills unfamiliar to medical graduates.

Let us consider some examples. We are inclined to make assumptions about the way things are but on enquiring into them in detail we may be alarmed to discover that our assumptions are incorrect and that things are not as good as we thought. For instance, do you know the answers to these questions in relation to the practice where you now work?

- Whether the women who attend the antenatal and postnatal clinics are happy with the service offered?

- How many elderly people suffer from incontinence?

- What proportion of school leavers have had booster doses of tetanus and polio vaccine?

- Whether there are any patients taking combinations of medicines which may interact?

It may be that enquiries would show that the service you provide is so good that everyone is satisfied, that all the school leavers are up to date with immunizations—or it may not. If indeed all is well then you can justifiably take pride in a thoroughly efficient, and probably unusual, practice. If, on the other hand, your project demonstrated a need to develop a service or to take action where that need was previously unknown or unrealized, then you have made the first step towards raising the standard of the service you offer.

Not only may a project be the exploration of the current state but it may be the initiation of a new service or development of an existing one. For instance, the setting up of a diabetic clinic or the introduction of physiotherapy or acupuncture are major developments with implications for staff, expenses, and the use of resources such as space and equipment. Such developments need experience to manage successfully, and the candidate for the MRCGP needs to show that the experience has been gained or at least that the implications of such a development have been understood. Projects of that kind may be outside the scope of a doctor still in training but the lessons should be learned in some way. Trainees should take every opportunity to be involved in the planning and decision-making in their training practices, for although trainees are theoretically supernumerary there is no reason why they should not participate in those processes.

However, not all developments need such extensive planning, and trainees are well placed to undertake some tasks themselves. Examples might be:

- Identifying defaulters from follow-up of patients for treatment of hypertension, identifying the reasons for default, and devising a system to reduce it

- Reviewing patients on hormone replacement therapy and developing a protocol for the management of HRT, if it did not already exist.

Audit

Audit should be seen as an important if demanding part of continuing education. It is the systematic recording of experience which can be used to influence subsequent policy decisions after suitable reflection and study of the matter concerned (Stanley et al., 1993). It implies the examination of one's own achievements with a view to making them as good as can be. It should be a normal part of professional activity, for one definition of a profession is a group of people who set and regulate their own standards of conduct and attainment. Marinker (1990) has defined medical audit as: "The attempt to improve the quality of medical care by measuring the performance of those providing that care, considering the performance in relation to desired standards, and by improving on that performance". Central to this is the idea that performance should be 'in relation to desired standards'. It is up to each of us as professional people to determine what that standard should be in our particular situation, for circumstances vary from place to place and practice to practice. It requires that we should know what can be done and how to do it, and that we should be able to show whether or not it has been done. Of course we cannot monitor everything that we do, nor can we do all the things that might be done, but we can develop an attitude of mind which is willing to allow some areas to be scrutinized in this way as examples of the range of activities we carry out. The attempt to achieve a high standard in one area must surely encourage us to demand and strive for high standards in others.

It is often said that general practice is so diverse and variable that no universal standard can be defined or expected. Indeed it is a complex and subtle system which is hard to evaluate as a whole; but that should not prevent a close examination of its components in an attempt to define specific areas to which a standard can be applied. For instance, if a decision is made to treat patients with long-term medication which might need adjustment or have side-effects or complications, it implies that there should be some follow-up system, which in turn leads to questions such as:

• Do the patients take their medication as intended?

• Do they come for the relevant checks?

• Do they get better as intended?

• If not, why not?

• What should be done to improve deficiencies?

• If a remedy for a deficiency has been applied, has it been effective?

Let us consider the example of the care of patients with raised blood pressure. This is a good example because the outcome of care can be measured with the sphygmomanometer (at least an intermediate outcome can be) and suitable guidelines for treatment and target blood pressure levels have been defined (British Hypertension Society, 1993). It is a simple clerical exercise to list the patients on treatment, check whether or not the patients have attended as expected, and whether the target levels have been reached. In cases where they have not been reached, attempts can be made to improve, and when the situation is reviewed after an appropriate interval it will be seen whether the desired standard has indeed been achieved. Similar exercises can be carried out for all patients in long-term care such as diabetics, epileptics, and people on long-term steroids, to name only a few.

The educational element comes in deciding what is the best course of action in the light of relevant and current published research and opinion, and in devising the standard which can be attained in the circumstances prevailing.

57

- What can we reasonably expect to achieve?
- If we are trying to reduce blood pressure, what is the best way to do it?
- To what level and in what proportion of patients can we expect to achieve that level?
- What research is there to guide us?
- If we are treating asthma, how do we know whether we are doing as well as we can?
- What are the indications for inhaled steroids?
- Have all our patients who need inhaled steroids been treated?
- Have they improved?
- How many of the cervical cytology reports we receive show an inadequate specimen?
- Is that better or worse than other people's results?
- Have all the abnormal results been dealt with properly?
- If not, why not?

Standard setting is the process by which we consider what level of attainment we think is ideal and how close we can get to the ideal in our individual circumstances. Audit then determines whether we have achieved what we intended.

What place has all this in the MRCGP examination? In the practice experience questionnaire there is a space to describe an audit or project which the candidate has carried out. It is likely to attract the examiners' attention in the first oral and a fluent and confident answer will score well. Even if it is not taken up in the examination, the insight gained by the exercise will strengthen the candidate's confidence and self-assurance and be evident to the oral examiners. Similarly questions in the critical reading question paper are designed to test candidates' ability to analyse and comment upon reports and other data presented in written or graphic form. The experience of preparing a project or audit will enhance the candidate's competence in doing that. To feel confident of success in these parts of the examination candidates are well advised to gain some experience in developing and implementing the kind of activities described.

References

British Hypertension Society (1993) Management guidelines in essential hypertension: Report of the Second Working Party of the British Hypertension Society. *British Medical Journal* **306**, 983–7.

Marinker M (Ed.) (1990) *Medical Audit in General Practice.* London, British Medical Journal.

Stanley I, Al-Shehri A and Thomas P (1993) Continuing education for general practice. 1. Experience, competence and the media of self-directed learning for established general practitioners. *British Journal of General Practice* **43**, 210–14.

7 Strategies for Preparation, Part 3

It is often not appreciated by those who are not concerned with it that general practice is a commercial enterprise as well as a health care organization and that the provision of health care can take place only within the fabric and constraints of the society it serves. The needs of one nation may be quite different from those of another, and the pressures and demands of one section of society within a nation may vary considerably from another. The effects of prosperity or poverty, of employment or unemployment, of housing or the lack of it are shown daily in the way in which people use their medical services, and the way those services are provided must take this into account.

Medicine and society

This is not the place to discuss this subject in detail, but it must be recognized that primary care is inextricably linked with the society it serves, and the candidate for the MRCGP should understand the way in which medical services are developed and provided. It is not simply knowing how to recognize and treat disease that makes a good general practitioner. How is that disease caused? Whom does it affect? How does it present, and what effect does it have on those it strikes, and on those close to the patient? What are the effects of poverty, housing, education, employment and environment? What can society do to maximize the health-giving factors and minimize those that cause disease? How much can medical services influence that society in changing towards a healthy state, and how much does that depend on other factors and other people? Should doctors take an active role in political pressure groups? How can we persuade those who have control of resources to use them most effectively where need is greatest?

The Royal College of General Practitioners has no 'political' stance in that it does not offer a radical solution to the nation's health problems based on social structure or political persuasion. It does, however, wish to influence provision of health care by offering advice where necessary based on the experience and researches of its members and others. Such advice is made available both to its members as part of the service of support and education, and also to government and other bodies interested in the provision of health care. Its members must be aware of all the influences that arise from the variations in social and material factors and bear upon health. While there has been a marvellous improvement in many areas of health care such as the control of infectious disease, the eradication of nutritional disorders like rickets and the introduction of safety measures in factories, there are still dangers that have not been eliminated and new hazards arise all too often.

Consider some of the following and their effect on the resources available to general practice:

- Contraception is technically advanced, but does everyone who needs it get it? If not, what are the consequences?

- The deprivation suffered by single parents of young children.

- Many people are better off financially and alcohol is relatively cheaper than it was; alcohol-related diseases are common.

- Food is plentiful and cheap, but not always well chosen.

- Obesity is frequent.

- Housing is still bad with overcrowding, homelessness and associated stresses.

- Aids.

- Child abuse.

- The Patient's Charter.

- Fundholding practices and trust hospitals.

- Major health screening programmes of cervical cytology and mammography. Do they improve health? Are they cost-effective? Could they be harmful?

- Do health promotion clinics promote better health? If so, do they reach the people who need them most?
- The inverse care law.

The list of topics which could be added is endless. None of those listed above can be meaningfully discussed without the views and needs of 'society' being taken into account. Medicine is now a major consumer of the nation's wealth, and it behoves doctors to ensure that while meeting the wishes of society on the one hand they also advise it on the benefits and losses, and the effectiveness of medical procedures on the other. This applies both at the collective level of society as a whole and at the individual level of the doctor-patient relationship. The College does not have a prescribed view on any of the topics outlined above, but the candidate for membership must show that he or she has addressed such matters in a considered way and is capable of taking a responsible and rational attitude to them.

The practice

The primary purpose of general practice is, of course, the care of patients who are ill or who have other medical needs, the promotion of health and the prevention of disease. This demands an organized framework, and as it has developed with the National Health Service general practice is based on a system of independent contractors. Thus general practitioners are themselves responsible for establishing the organizations through which they can meet their contractual obligations, and this imposes on them a variety of obligations which doctors in many disciplines do not have. Therefore candidates in the MRCGP must expect to be examined in those areas and will need to prepare themselves accordingly.

Reference has already been made in Chapter 5 to 'The practice' as one of the contents of the examination. The subdivisions of this are shown in Table 7.1. It is essential to gain experience of these areas while preparing for practice, but they are easily overlooked because they are not matters which patients present to their doctors and are often seen as someone else's responsibility. It is too late to wait until something has gone wrong in your practice to discover that

Table 7.1 Topics to be considered relating to the practice

- Practice management
- The team
- Financial matters
- Premises and equipment
- Medical records
- Medico-legal matters
- Research

you are responsible for its organization, and for its failures as well as its successes.

The trainee and recent entrant to the profession must take an interest in all that goes on in the practice; see what is happening and who does what; and discover how the systems in use have been devised and developed. Practices vary in their organization and adapt to meet their individual needs, and there are many ways to achieve the same purpose. It is important therefore to see as wide a range of practices as possible to get a broad experience. Nevertheless, underlying this variety of systems there are needs common to all such organizations in order to meet the obligations imposed on them by law and by the Terms and Conditions of Service in the NHS. Candidates should therefore pay attention not only to the systems in their own practices and in any other practices they visit, but should read textbooks on practice management and the law as it applies to employment, and become familiar with the maintenance of equipment, the keeping of records, accounts, partnership agreements and disputes. Such matters as practice reports, complaints procedures for patients, and the construction and maintainance of practice premises may arise infrequently in the experience of doctors new to the profession, but it is important to be familiar with their principles even if the details need to be worked out at the relevant time.

Practice management

Although the management of the practice business may be delegated, responsibility for it remains with the partners who own the business. They must determine the policy of the practice, who is to be employed to achieve that, and where and how the practice is to function and to what standard. They must determine what services are to be provided and how the patients will have access to them. They must put in place whatever structure is needed and see that it works, that it is paid for and conforms to the law. They must account for the taxes that apply to both them and their staff. When that has been done and the fees collected and the expenses paid, they will draw the profit from the practice as their incomes and must decide how that is to be determined and divided between them. To do all this requires some understanding of management techniques, and time and effort spent in such studies will be well rewarded.

The team

Such is the diversity of skills needed to provide effective primary care it is no longer possible for the general practitioner to provide them alone. Here again practices vary in the extent to which they have developed multidisciplinary teams and it may be necessary for candidates to broaden their experience beyond that of the individual practice. It is important to know and understand the duties and skills, and indeed the limitations, of a variety of workers. The main disciplines are shown in Table 7.2.

Table 7.2 Members of the primary care team

- Health visitors
- Practice nurses
- District nurses
- Community psychiatric nurses
- Physiotherapists
- Midwives

- Receptionists
- Secretaries
- Counsellors
- Social workers
- Chiropodists
- and others

As the National Health Service has developed, some of these workers have been employed by local health authorities and seconded to primary care, while in others general practitioners have employed them directly. They may or may not work from the same premises. In any event the doctor must be able to relate well to them and know how and when to use their services appropriately and effectively. The management of a team consisting of several disciplines and provided by different authorities, or even by self-employed professional workers, requires skill and tact and an understanding of their respective talents and responsibilities.

Financial matters

Typically doctors are not renowned for their financial expertise, though this seems to be changing as practices develop the trend towards more accountability. In the National Health Service doctors do not handle money personally to any great extent, neither taking it in payment for goods or services nor in transactions or purchases on a regular basis. Yet we all like to have enough of it, and without it our activities are restricted. It is therefore important to manage the finances of a practice well. Where a practice has a turnover of several hundred thousand pounds, a saving of 1 or 2 per cent may amount to several thousand pounds—enough perhaps to pay for an extra member of staff.

Candidates should understand the sources of money, and how it is budgeted and accounted for; how practice expenses in staff wages, heat, light, repairs, purchases of drug stocks and equipment are paid for and recorded. It is essential to understand how various incomes, whether NHS or private, are received and recorded, and how at the end of the year accounts are examined by the accountant, tax liabilities met and the practice profit share finalized. The wise general practitioner is also competent in business matters: the MRCGP candidate should be able to show some of that wisdom.

Premises and equipment

Modern general practice requires proper premises, whether purpose built or adapted, and a range of equipment that is complex and expensive. Partnerships may invest thousands of pounds in this, which can enhance the practice income if done well or be wasteful if done thoughtlessly. Similarly ownership or tenancy of property, the admission of the public to these premises, and the employment of people there are subject to legislation. The candidate must know how such laws apply and how they should be implemented. Health and Safety Regulations, Public Liability Insurance, contracts of employment for staff, and such mundane matters as the Uniform Business Rate all fall within this field. They may be very boring to the aspiring partner, but there is a business to run and even if maximizing the profit is not the prime motive of the partnership, legal and financial obligations must be met.

Medical records

Records are important for at least two reasons, namely the efficient and effective delivery of medical care and medico-legal security. Therefore decisions must be made about what form they should take. Some questions to be decided about records are shown in Table 7.3. The candidate should give some thought to these questions, and although decisions about them may vary from practice to practice and be made by others in training practices, responsibility for them will soon fall upon the new entrant to practice. Education in this area is therefore a necessary part of preparation for the examination.

Table 7.3 What should the records be like?

- What information should be recorded?
- Should records be paper or computerized?
- How are they to be kept and stored?
- Who may have access to them and for what purpose?
- Under what circumstances may patients see the records?
- What may be divulged to third parties?
- What constitutes consent for divulging information?
- How may records be used for research?

Medico-legal matters

This is an area of increasing importance, but one in which it is tempting to put one's head in the sand and hope that problems will not arise. It is most commonly met in the form of requests for information from solicitors acting on behalf of a patient, and, of course, general practitioners will usually be pleased to help their patients in difficulty and may charge for doing so. The certification of deaths and reporting certain deaths to the coroner or procurator fiscal are legal duties for doctors, who also have legal obligations concerning the purchase, storage, prescription and administration of drugs, and in such areas as the Mental Health Act and intervention in cases of child abuse.

Ethics

Closely related to medico-legal matters, ethics in general practice often present difficult dilemmas. When is it right (if ever) to divulge information without the consent of the patient? Where is the line drawn between extreme pain relief in terminal care and euthanasia? What do you do if you know one of your patients is a felon? Or if someone asks you to issue a false certificate? Fortunately such occasions are infrequent, but all too real. The candidate must be prepared to answer some, albeit hypothetical, questions in the MRCGP examination.

Research

Not all general practitioners will be interested in or able to undertake research, but everyone depends on the researches of others to guide his or her own efforts effectively. The first oral examination provides an opportunity for candidates to describe their own research work, and this opportunity should be taken as extra marks can be obtained if it is done well. Even though the candidate may have done no research personally an understanding of how general practice has been guided by relevant research, how to interpret it and how to introduce the changes it indicates are all important aspects of preparation for the examination. The CRQ paper has been developed to test ability in this area. In future, as public accountability and the promotion of high standards become increasingly relevant and important, so candidates must be able to show their ability to respond to its implications.

Finally, candidates must be able to show that they can organize themselves, delegate, work in a team and relate to colleagues, both doctors and other professionals. The ability to communicate and co-operate with both patients and colleagues is an essential characteristic of a competent general practitioner and is therefore carefully assessed in the examination.

8 Answering the MCQ

The preparations discussed in Chapters 5, 6 and 7 are, in effect, preparation for practice rather than for examination, but of course the candidate is interested in maximizing the score obtained when he or she chooses to be tested. For this reason it is important to understand what qualities the examiners are seeking and how they assess them and award marks. This and subsequent chapters describe how the questions and the marking schedules are devised, so that candidates can organize their answers most appropriately.

The MCQ

The multiple choice question paper is intended to assess only factual knowledge and there is little or no room for discretion in giving an answer: it is either right or wrong. The whole range of knowledge required by a general practitioner is tested, including ethical and legal topics and practice organization. The balance of subjects within the total questions may vary from time to time. The present distribution (1993) is shown in Table 8.1. The table has been constructed to show the approximate distribution between clinical and non-clinical subjects but it must be remembered that within a single stem there may be a variety of emphases. Thus one stem on, say, alcohol abuse may deal with both its clinical presentation and its social effects; or another on epilepsy may ask about both its therapy and its implications for a driving licence.

Marks are now awarded on a true/false basis, that is to say the candidate is asked to say whether the statement is true or false, and gains one mark if the answer given is right and none if it is wrong. Since the recent abolition of negative marking for an incorrect

---

Table 8.1 The balance of subjects within the MCQ

- **Clinical**

  Medicine 60

  Psychiatry 36

  Therapeutics 36

  Obstetrics and gynaecology 36

  Paediatrics 30

  Dermatology 24

  Physical medicine and trauma 18

  Ophthalmology 18

  Surgical diagnosis 18

  Ear, nose and throat 12

  Infectious diseases 12

  Care of the elderly 12

- **Non-clinical**

  Practice organization 24

  Ethical and legal 12

  Epidemiology and research 12

- **Extended matching question**

---

answer there is no penalty for being wrong, so attempting as many questions as possible is likely to increase the marks gained. Many questions can be answered after a little thought on the basis of other knowledge or experience, or on probability: for instance, whether there is a 'likelihood' of a diagnosis of appendicitis being correct when the patient's temperature is less than 39°C. It may be that the precise statistic on this point escapes you in the examination, but a moment's reflection on your experience will tell you that most patients with appendicitis are not very feverish. This is not the same as guessing, which implies giving an answer without reason or evidence. If experience tells you something, use it! It is therefore good policy to work through the paper answering questions to which you can give answers confidently and quickly, and then return to reconsider those about which you are less certain. Candidates are, in fact, encouraged to attempt as many questions as possible, for not only does this increase their probability of a high score but it also improves discrimination between good and not-so-good.

One feature of MCQs which often causes comment is the wording of the stem. In the MRCGP it is not the policy to ask trick or cryptic questions and the words in the stem should be taken to mean what they normally do.

The word 'characteristic' implies that the feature mentioned is always or nearly always present, or that it refers to a diagnostic feature whose absence would cast doubt on the diagnosis. (For example, alcohol-dependent patients characteristically develop delirium tremens on withdrawal within three days.)

'Typical' implies that it is expected but not invariable or essential in the given situation.

'Recognized' means that such a feature has been reliably described but may be present only occasionally. Similarly 'associated with' suggests a well-described but occasional presence.

'Never' and 'always' are words that should be used carefully in medicine, for any rule may have its exceptions. The answer to a question using these words is therefore likely to be false.

'The majority of cases' means over 50%.

Where a figure is given, for example '30% of cases', this is usually a rounded up figure; some authorities may say 28%, others 32%, but there is a consensus in that range. If you think it is about right, the answer is probably 'true'.

Sometimes the stems are phrased in such a way as to demand careful thought. For instance, it may be put in the negative: "In presbyacusis the hearing by bone conduction is unaffected." The correct answer is 'false' of course; the hearing is *not* *un*affected.

Similarly the opposite of the truth may be cited; for example: "In epiglottitis the onset is typically insidious." The correct answer here would be 'false', for the onset is anything but that, hence the urgency the condition demands.

Some multiple choice questions that have been used in the past are given in Appendix 6.

It should be remembered that some questions are used which only very knowledgeable candidates will answer correctly. Few candidates score more than 70% in the MCQ, and a good mark is in the region of 60%. No one can know everything. However, candidates will wish to score as many marks as they can, and therefore it is worth reiterating that as many questions as possible should be attempted, for though nothing will be gained by a wrong answer neither will anything be lost.

The extended matching question

In addition to the conventional kind of MCQ question, from October 1993 the new form of extended matching question will be introduced, on a trial basis at first, that is not counting towards total marks, as described in Chapter 3. This is similar in form to the extended matching question introduced for the first time in the MEQ of the May 1993 examination, but in the MCQ it is used to test basic knowledge and the ability to apply that knowledge to a clinical situation.

An example of the extended matching question is given in Table 8.2, where the theme is indicated and there are a list of diagnostic 'options' which must be matched with the case history 'items', the correct answer being the one which is most likely to be the diagnosis in a general practice setting. There will usually be several options, more than the number of items, so not all the options will be used. Furthermore, any option may be correct for more than one item. For instance, there may be two items describing different presenting symptoms or signs of two patients who have the same diagnosis.

Each option is identified by a capital letter, and to answer the question the candidate must write this letter beside the relevant item. It is very important to realize that one, and only one, letter

Table 8.2 An example of an extended matching question

Theme: Reduced vision in the eye

Option list

(A) Basilar migraine   (F) Occlusion of the central retinal vein

(B) Cerebral tumour   (G) Optic neuritis (demyelinating)

(C) Cranial arteritis   (H) Retinal detachment

(D) Macular degeneration   (I) Tobacco optic neuropathy

(E) Occlusion of the central retinal artery

Instruction

For each patient with reduced vision select the most likely diagnosis. Each option can be used once, more than once, or not at all. Only *one* option should be selected for each item.

Items

361 A 75-year-old man, who is a heavy smoker, with a blood pressure of 170/105, complains of floaters in the right eye for many months and flashing lights in bright sunlight. He has now noticed a 'curtain' across vision in the right eye.

362 A 70-year-old woman complains of shadows which sometimes obscure her vision for a few minutes. She has felt unwell recently with loss of weight and face pain when chewing food.

363 A 45-year-old woman, who is a heavy smoker, with a blood pressure of 170/110, complains of impaired vision in the left eye. She has difficulty discriminating colours and notices that her eye aches when looking to the side.

Answer sheet

For each item number, enter *only one* of the letters given above, to indicate your choice from the option list.

361 .... (Correct answer H)

362 .... (Correct answer C)

363 .... (Correct answer G)

may be used; to hedge one's bets by placing more than one will score no mark, even if one of them is correct. Each item correctly matched scores one mark, and no mark is lost for an incorrect answer. A different answer form is used for the extended matching question from that for the stem and item form, which is optically scanned.

When answering this type of question it is best to read through the items, or clinical situations, before looking at the options list. A provisional diagnosis can then be made and the option list of diagnoses examined to see if it is included. It is important not to use the option list as a mental checklist for each item because this will take much longer than the 60 seconds per item that has been allocated.

9 Answering the MEQ

In the MCQ the candidates have been tested on their familiarity with the basic knowledge required for general practice. The MEQ has a totally different objective, namely to assess how they might perform in the 'real world', where patients present in a wide variety of ways, and problems of management, communication and policy must be dealt with by doctors and their colleagues.

The nature of general practice

General practice is by its very nature a wide-ranging discipline. It is that branch of medicine to which access is available to anyone who considers himself to be ill in any way, the definition of 'illness' being chosen by the applicant and not by the doctor. At this point the illness is undefined and indicates only that the person concerned does not have the usual sense of well-being. Whether that lack of well-being is due to physical disease, psychological disorder or to personal or other circumstances has yet to be defined. The person who presents may not even be the person who has the problem that has caused the presentation.

Once the problem has been defined it may become apparent that other people are affected by it too or that there are consequences to family members, workmates or society as a whole. Problems may present as emergencies that are dealt with in hospital or elsewhere but cause complications or difficulties later. There are matters like preventive medicine, the assessment of risk factors, and the need to recommend changes in lifestyle. Furthermore, and by no means unimportantly, general practice is a business needing medical and administrative staff who must communicate with each other and be competent in finance and management. All these areas and more must be within the competence of the general practitioner. The MEQ paper is designed to test the range and depth of such competences. Indeed any question may refer to several of them.

Using knowledge

For this reason candidates must be aware that answers to questions which deal simply with the clinical presentation and ignore the wider implications may be inadequate. For instance, a question might deal with the presentation of a man aged 50 years with a raised blood pressure, and ask: "What would you hope to achieve in this consultation?" Clearly it would not be enough to answer: "Prescribe medication to lower it." Other matters would need to be considered too, such as whether there were other risk factors, the implications for the patient's work, and his own ideas and anxieties about what this development might mean for his future health.

Some of the topics which have often been the subject of questions in recent years are shown in Table 9.1. Study of this list will indicate that this is quite a different situation from the MCQ, where only knowledge is tested. In the MEQ knowledge is important, but the real test is: "How does the candidate use the knowledge he or she possesses to resolve the problem that has been presented; how broad a range of ideas does the candidate have; and how well justified are the statements that are made?"

Marking schedule

The questions are marked using a schedule developed by those examiners who are marking each question. There are normally 10 questions, each marked by a group of five or six examiners. In preparation for their annual workshop all examiners in the MEQ groups answer the draft questions 'under examination conditions', that is in the time normally allowed and without recourse to books. This forms a kind of collective wisdom within the group, and from this the examiners compile a list of the features which they think

Table 9.1 Some common topics and themes in the MEQ papers in recent years

- All aspects of clinical and preventive medicine
- 'Problem' and 'difficult' patients
- Psychological problems in individuals and families
- The consultation process
- Practice organization
- Relationships with colleagues and others
- Controversial and new topics
- The doctor's own feelings and awareness
- Ethics and attitudes
- Unusual and original ideas such as the 'matching pairs' questions

are essential to a good answer. There may be several such features, or 'constructs', in a question, but usually three to five. The list is then amplified with notes of the essential points of each construct, and forms the 'marking schedule'. The examiner's task is to see whether the candidate has identified the various constructs in the schedule and award a mark for each one according to how well it has been described and discussed. Marks are awarded on a scale of 0 to 5. If the candidate omits to mention it at all the score is 0; if it is clearly identified, and fully and rationally discussed, it gains 5.

To gain good marks the answer does not have to be a stylish, detailed and grammatically perfect treatise with references, but it should be as comprehensive and practical as the 12 minutes allowed for each question permit. It may be given in the form of a short essay, but it may be clearer and quicker to set it out in note form, as tables under headings, or as a flow-chart if that seems appropriate. Whatever form is chosen it should be legible; hasty writing may get more words on the paper but will not score marks if the examiner cannot read them!

Examples

Example 9.1

Consider the example of a question from a recent paper. The MEQ had started by saying that the setting was a practice of a certain size and nature, and that you were engaged in a typical morning surgery. Questions related to the patients attending, and one was as follows:

Mrs Brown, aged 52, is your next patient. She enquires about hormone replacement therapy because she has heard that it helps to prevent future osteoporosis. What factors would you like to take into account in considering your reply?

Note that the question is not phrased: "What are the advantages and disadvantages of hormone replacement therapy?" That was the form of the old practice topic question which was abandoned as being unreliable. It is set in the 'real world' of the surgery, with a 'real' patient asking a pertinent question. Nor is the question simply about whether HRT would be good for Mrs Brown. It starts with her enquiry, specifically about prevention of osteoporosis, and invites the candidate to expand on other aspects of HRT which might be relevant in Mrs Brown's case.

It would be possible to answer by writing a monograph on HRT, but there are only 12 minutes available; or to say: "Take a full history", but that misses the point; or to list the causes of osteoporosis, but that leaves the patient out of it. This question is asking how you will meet Mrs Brown's enquiry, and deal with her implied proposal that she might start HRT.

A marking schedule for this question might contain four constructs, such as:

- How much does the candidate respect the individuality and autonomy of the patient?

- How well does the candidate communicate with the patient?

- To what extent does the candidate take the patient's health beliefs into account?

- How clearly does the candidate demonstrate an understanding of the relevant clinical knowledge about the therapy and its potential to prevent morbidity in later life?

An answer simply setting out the four areas above might score a mark or two for each in that they have all been touched on. However, to gain adequate marks there must be some discussion. For instance, under the construct of health beliefs the following might be mentioned:

- What are Mrs Brown's own views?

- How did she form those views?

- Does she have any incorrect beliefs?

- Are there any conflicting beliefs?

Similarly under the heading of communication, what is the candidate going to communicate, and how? The following might be mentioned:

- Advantages and disadvantages of HRT

- Risks and side-effects, e.g. withdrawal bleeds

- Follow-up procedures, involvement of practice nurse

- Giving Mrs Brown the opportunity to reply, and checking her understanding.

Some other recent MEQ questions are given in Examples 9.2, 9.3 and 9.4, chosen to show how topics are taken from the various aspects of clinical work and practice organization. These examples also have an outline of the constructs contained in the marking schedule as illustrations. As an exercise, take a few minutes to visualize the scene depicted in each of them. Then read the constructs in turn, and write down a specimen answer to each one, expressing each of the points mentioned in each construct, taking as much time to do so as you wish. If you do not feel confident in the area of any particular construct, perhaps it would be worth reading around the subject and then repeating the exercise.

Example 9.2

During morning surgery, 20-year-old Debbie T brings her only child Craig, aged three and a quarter. Debbie says: "Craig doesn't eat a thing!" The child appears well-nourished but slightly withdrawn, and there are no obvious features to suggest he is unwell.

Describe your approach to this problem.

This question, like most in the MEQ, allows a good candidate to show comprehension of the many implications of general practice problems. These include:

- **Making contact with the patient:** Does the candidate display awareness of possible communication difficulties and have a variety of strategies to overcome them? A poor candidate may ignore this issue or mention it only in passing. A better one might describe ways to build solid rapport with Debbie, and comment on their effectiveness.

- **Child development:** Does the candidate show an understanding of normal child development? Clearly organic disease needs to be considered, and the good candidate would briefly but comprehensively describe a plan for doing this.

- **Warning signs of abuse:** Does the candidate explicitly recognize this as a possibility, with all its implications?

- **Hidden agendas:** Does the candidate appreciate that Debbie's stated worry about the child may be her 'ticket of admission' to discuss other underlying problems of her own? A good candidate would describe this phenomenon and suggest a range of possible physical, psychological and social agendas.

- **Management options:** Can the candidate suggest, evaluate and select from among a range of sensible and appropriate clinical management plans?

- **Health beliefs:** Does the candidate recognize the importance of a patient's health beliefs and the factors that may influence them in this case? A good answer would give some examples of possible cultural influences on Debbie, and describe how they may affect the management and outcome.

This question was set on 6 May 1992.

Example 9.3

(This question may have surprised some candidates, coming as it did in the same paper as, and immediately following, Example 9.2.)

The very next patient is 4-year-old Kylie, accompanied by her mother Elaine S, aged 22. Elaine says: "I'm worried about Kylie. She's such a picky eater, and doesn't eat enough to keep a sparrow alive."

Describe how and why your response to this presentation might be affected by the previous consultation with Debbie T and Craig.

Candidates who failed to stop and read the question were tempted into repeating substantially their answers to the previous question in this paper (given here as Example 9.2). This would have scored no marks. The question is not about the management of maternal anxiety; rather, it is intended to elicit candidates' appreciation of the factors affecting how doctors respond to a succession of apparently similar problems.

To score well the candidate would need to discuss:

- **A balanced approach:** Can the candidate recognize and deal with such negative reactions as boredom, suspicion, irritation, frustration and a tendency to reiterate a stereotyped response? More positive responses would be to recognize where the similarities and differences between the two cases might lie, and to understand the importance of maintaining interest and empathy.

- **Effective management:** Can the candidate make use of the similarities and differences to tailor an effective management plan? An individual appraisal of the second case is clearly called for, avoiding uncritical repetition of what had been described in the preceding one. On the other hand, the doctor might now be more 'in the groove', so that there are positive advantages to having been primed by Debbie and Craig.

- **Extraneous factors:** Is the candidate aware of factors outside the consulting room that might need thought or action? What are the social and educational differences between the two mothers, and do they matter? Why have children's eating patterns suddenly become an issue? Has there been a television programme about them, or a scandal in the local paper? Is the practice's programme of regular child surveillance functioning effectively? Is the health visitor appropriately involved? A good candidate would be alert to such background issues as these.

This question was set on 6 May 1992.

Example 9.4

The MEQ paper usually contains at least one question intended to signal the constantly evolving priorities and emphases within general practice and in the arena of vocational training. This is a good example of such a question.

Your correspondence in-tray contains a mounting number of leaflets and brochures advertising meetings and courses approved for the postgraduate education allowance (PGEA). How do you decide which, if any, to attend?

An ideal answer to this question would show appreciation of the following issues:

- **Educational need:** Personal self-assessment and audit; the needs of the practice and its individual members; the course's content and categorization; personal interest in the material

- **The educational process:** The relative merits of formats such as lecture, seminar, distance learning package; the credentials of the organizers and presenters; the degree of 'consumer-centredness'

- **Logistics:** Location, timing, personal and practice convenience; availability of locum cover

- **Finance:** Cost of the course weighed against PGEA income or the course's interests and merits

- **Other considerations:** For example: promotional sponsorship; attractiveness of course, venue, and facilities; need for relaxation and recreation as well as stimulation.

This question was set on 10 October 1991.

Towards an ideal answer

When these answers have been practised move on to the examples in Appendix 7, and write answers under examination conditions. It might be helpful to write these in conjunction with other candidates, so that the various answers could be compared, thereby revealing ideas which might have escaped you working alone. An 'ideal' answer might then be contrived.

Ask yourself:

- What are the essential and critical features of this situation?
- What could a good doctor do in this case?
- What alternatives for action are there here?
- What are my reasons and justifications for actions proposed?

Although the examiners have extracted the essentials from the question after much thought, the candidates have no such luxury, and their answers are not expected to match the examiners' analysis word for word. It may be that points from one or more constructs are given in different parts of the answer; it is the examiners' task to look for them. It is unlikely that any one answer will cover all the points in the schedule. An answer might omit one construct altogether but that might not matter if the others are dealt with very well. Remember, the examiners ask themselves: "Has this candidate identified all the constructs?" and "How well does the candidate express his or her understanding of this construct?" Maximum marks are therefore gained both by identifying the constructs and dealing with them in reasonable detail.

In effect it is not the total marks scored individually which determines success, but rather the marks relative to other candidates; in other words, the rank ordering. It may not matter that you have not noticed all the points in the question, so long as you have done as well as, or better than your fellow candidates—assuming they are typical of previous cohorts of candidates.

On the day

How then should one approach the MEQ paper on the examination day? The following ideas may help:

- Be relaxed! Take time to arrive early and without haste.

83

- Read the instructions at the beginning of the paper carefully; they may have been changed recently.

- Keep track of time as you work through the paper; do not spend so much time on one question that you run short on others, because:

- You must answer all the questions; omission of one will lose one tenth of your possible marks.

- Read each question carefully, word by word and clause by clause. They have been very carefully constructed, and virtually every word is significant.

- Think yourself into the scene depicted in the question and consider all the characters, whether they are explicitly mentioned or not.

- Ask yourself: "What do the examiners have in mind in this question?" "What are its essential and critical features?" "Where is it capable of leading my thoughts?"

- Write legibly; fewer words written slowly may say more than many in haste.

- Make your answers meaningful; waffle scores very few marks!

- Set the answers out clearly and tidily.

- Remember to keep all your answers on the relevant page, and do not refer to other pages. The pages go to different groups of examiners who will not understand your references.

A broad approach

The format of the MEQ is always under review, and that outlined above will undoubtedly change as time goes by. Indeed the MEQ has a tradition of including a question, often the last one, which takes the unwary candidate by surprise. Merely preparing for conventional questions with stock answers risks exposing the weaknesses of a narrow approach to general practice. On the other hand, candidates whose outlook and experience are broad, and whose knowledge and perception extends beyond what has been addressed in previous examinations will find that the MEQ is an opportunity in which their wider approaches will be rewarded.

This approach is part of the MRCGP examination's secondary but important role as a contributor to the agenda for learning. Recent examples include questions on alcoholism and Aids before these topics were perceived as important in general practice. Other topics that have been introduced in this way are the importance of family history in disease (in which a genogram was presented for comment), transcultural factors in medicine and, most recently, the literature on the consultation (tested by the innovation of the extended matching question).

Having taken the MCQ and the MEQ in the morning of the examination day the candidates have a break for lunch and return, one hopes, refreshed and eager to write their answers to the critical reading paper.

10 Answering the CRQ

The critical reading question paper (CRQ) was introduced in 1990 in order to examine candidates' ability to read, understand and act upon the increasingly large amount of published and unpublished literature and other material which now confronts the general practitioner. The objectives of the paper are therefore to assess the ability of the candidates in the following areas:

- Evaluation of published literature relevant to general practice, and application of the lessons learned from it in their own practices

- Analysis of written material and data presented graphically such as protocols for disease management, audit findings, and reports of various kinds

- Ability to make decisions, in both the clinical field and practice management, that take into account scientific evidence published in the general professional literature

- Familiarity with important current issues in general practice and ability to evaluate the differing views and opinions that prevail

- Knowledge of clinical epidemiology and its application to general practice.

The new CRQ

Experience with the new paper has shown that it performs well and reliably (Foulkes, 1992) but as with any innovation there is some room for improvement. Consequently, with effect from 1994 the form in which the paper is presented will be revised, though it will not be radically different. The way in which it is presented remains unchanged; namely, like the MEQ, in the form of a booklet with a series of questions at the top of each page and space for answers below the question and overleaf. The pages are separated and sent to different examiners, so answers must be confined to the relevant pages.

The new form of CRQ will have 10 questions. The expansion to 10 is intended to improve its reliability, but it will also need more time to answer. Two and a half hours will now be allowed, which includes some time to read the presented material. There will be more items of material presented but they will be shorter than in recent papers. In the original form the first part, containing three questions, was devoted to a whole article from a journal such as the *British Medical Journal* or *British Journal of General Practice* and somewhat overshadowed the article. In the revised form there will be less emphasis on the whole article; four or five short extracts will be presented and a question asked about each of them. Other material such as figures from a practice audit or a protocol for disease management will also be presented and the questions will seek critical observations about them.

This modification has an important implication for candidates preparing for the examination. When so much weight was given to a paper from a journal it appeared that books were of lesser importance because so much of the examination was devoted to material recently published in a journal. That was not so, of course, but there was little scope for including questions which related to books. In the new form there will be more recognition of the part that books play in education for practice, particularly in that part which deals with candidates' knowledge and understanding of the current literature. It is reasonable to assume that in this context 'current' means literature that has been published in the last three years or so.

Current format

The CRQ paper now falls into two parts, each of which contains five questions.

Part 1 assesses candidates' familiarity with and understanding of recent literature, both in books and journals, relating to general practice. Questions are based on common and important areas of interest which are currently relevant or are the subject of public or professional debate.

Part 2 examines candidates' ability to read in a critical and discriminating way, and to draw conclusions and propose actions in the light of that reading. Questions are based on material presented to the candidate in the examination paper, which may be part of a published article, a report, protocol or guidelines, or the result of an audit or other analytical exercise.

The questions are devised in much the same way as the other written parts of the examination, in that a small group of examiners drafts the questions. These are then answered by the other CRQ examiners 'under examination conditions' and the ideas generated thereby are collected and discussed by the groups of examiners who will mark each question. A list of the essential features which a good answer would contain is prepared. There may be six or seven such features in a CRQ question, or even more. A good answer will discuss each feature in some detail rather than simply mentioning it. To gain good marks, therefore, candidates must be able to recognize as many features as possible and discuss them well.

Marking scale

The examiner's task is to ask: "How well does this candidate express his or her understanding of this point?" Marks are not awarded numerically but according to a scale of categories which goes from 'Excellent' through 'Very good', 'Good', 'Satisfactory' and 'Not very good' to 'Unsatisfactory' and 'Bad'. The examiner records the decisions on a specially designed grid, and this information is then converted by computer into a rank ordering of all the results. In practice the majority of answers fall in the range 'Good', 'Satisfactory' or 'Not very good', with about 15% in the top two and another 15% in the bottom two categories.

In the critical reading question paper the level of 'Satisfactory' will be attained by a candidate who indicates a clear understanding of the issues raised in the questions but without referring to supporting evidence; to score better than that requires that the evidence on which the candidate bases his or her opinions should be provided by naming the published work, whether it be a book, a paper or the report of a working party or other source. Naming the author or journal or date of publication will not in itself gain marks, nor would they be deducted if not given, but doing so with confidence would emphasize a candidate's familiarity with and knowledge of the material quoted. The ability to see both sides of an argument, the advantages and disadvantages, and to adopt a personal view based on rational evidence is what will gain the best marks. As in the MEQ, answers may be given in expanded note form. A fluent and aptly worded essay is not expected, but a clear, legible and logically constructed summary of the candidate's thinking will convey all that is necessary to obtain an appropriate mark.

Devising an answer

In devising an answer it is vital to understand the question. The wording has been very carefully chosen to provide maximum opportunity to discuss the topic in question, and though the question is brief nearly every word is significant. It pays therefore to consider the wording in some detail for a few moments before plunging into the answer, and to consider:

- Why is this question being asked?
- What are the controversial issues it contains?
- What have I read about this, and in which book or journal?
- What does my experience teach me in relation to what I have read?
- What are the significant words in the question?

Example 10.1

For example, in the October 1992 examination there was the following question:

Summarize current thinking on the use of drugs in the management of chronic asthma.

The topic may have been chosen for the following reasons:

- Asthma is a common, disabling and life-threatening disease in which chronic symptoms may be denied or unrecognized by the patient and even the doctor; symptoms previously not recognized as due to asthma are now seen to be so; and management of chronic asthma is mostly carried out in general practice.

- Despite much attention to asthma and the introduction of effective drugs it is increasing in incidence and mortality rates have not been reduced.

- There are several types of drug available with a variety of delivery systems, and there have been significant changes recently in recommendations for their use.

Issues that are recent or controversial include:

- The role of preventive drugs

- The place of steroids, inhaled or oral, in the condition

- The degree to which patients are involved in monitoring their symptoms and modifying their treatment

- The ideas and opinions of patients in relation to long-term medication, particularly with steroids

- The implications for supervision of medication in asthma clinics run by nurses.

Recent publications include:

- A major paper published in the *British Medical Journal* (British Thoracic Society, 1990) and many other publications

Candidates should be familiar with the subject:

- Asthma is a common and important condition of which every candidate should have had considerable experience.

The question has been set to assess the competence of candidates in a changing field. The significant words are:

- 'Current thinking'

- 'Drugs'

- 'Chronic'.

The question does not ask: "How does the candidate treat chronic asthma?" but "What are the ideas about it that prevail in the profession as a whole?" It does ask about drugs, so other forms of treatment such as acupuncture or psychotherapy, even if of proven value, would not be of relevance in this question. It also specifies the chronic state, so time spent discussing the management of acute attacks would gain no marks however good the account was.

A candidate who is well prepared will have a sound knowledge of the subject from textbooks and other sources, and have modified this appropriately by reading the journals. He or she will have had sufficient practical experience to understand the importance of the topic, and would probably agree with the statements made above about significance of chronic asthma. How might those qualities be used to write a good answer? The principal features of a good answer are shown in Table 10.1.

Table 10.1 The principal features of a good answer to Example 10.1

- A description of the general practitioner's role in the management of chronic asthma

- Reference to the underestimate of the disability and mortality it causes

- The place of drugs in the avoidance of disability and life-threatening episodes, and in the reduction of mortality

- A list of the drugs available and their indications

- Reference to the British Thoracic Society's guidelines as well as other significant publications

- An indication of the importance of effective patient education towards understanding the disease and monitoring its severity so that drugs can be used most appropriately and effectively

---

An answer which outlined those areas might score well in some places but would not be more than satisfactory if no more detail were given. For instance in the part about drugs the relative benefits and problems of each, the available delivery systems and their appropriate use could be listed. When and how to use them, and perhaps a protocol for their use, could be described. Similarly, in referring to patient education, the importance of the patient knowing when to modify treatment and when to seek advice, and of teaching and monitoring inhaler technique could be discussed. Reference to the guidelines by implication would be adequate, but mentioning them by name and emphasizing the stress they place upon the timely use of steroids, for instance, would perhaps raise the grading from 'Satisfactory' to 'Good' or 'Very good' for that section.

It is recognized, of course, that there is a limited time in which to answer each question. Few candidates are going to cover all the points contained in the marking schedule in the 12–15 minutes available. The judgements examiners make about the answers take this into account, so that 'Satisfactory' and 'Excellent' are relevant to what a competent doctor should be able to set out in those circumstances. Nevertheless a good candidate will have most, if not all, those ideas in mind and will be able to set them out briefly and clearly in the examination situation. If they are not in your mind when you enter the examination hall you will have a problem.

Example 10.1 is typical of the kind of question which might occur in Part one of the revised form of the CRQ paper. Examples 10.2 and 10.3 are past questions of the type which would now occur in Part 2 and Tables 10.2 and 10.3 indicate how the examiners interpreted the questions. These are based upon the actual marking schedules, and are published with permission (Dwyer D, Southgate L, personal communications).

Example 10.2

The following example about a published paper was Question 1A in the May 1993 examination. The whole paper except the abstract was presented in the examination. To save space, only the abstract is given here, which is done with permission.

General practice consultations: is there any point in being positive? Thomas KB (1987) *British Medical Journal* **294**, 1200–2.

Abstract

A group of 200 patients who presented in general practice with symptoms but no abnormal physical signs and in whom no definite diagnosis was made were randomly selected for one of four consultations: a consultation conducted in a 'positive manner', with and without treatment, and a consultation conducted in a 'non-positive manner', called a negative consultation, with and without treatment.

Two weeks after consultation there was a significant difference in patient satisfaction between the positive and negative groups but not between the treated and untreated groups. Similarly, 64% of those receiving a positive consultation got better, compared with 39% of those who received a negative consultation (p=0.001) and 53% of those treated got better compared with 50% of those not treated (p=0.5).

Discuss the strengths and weaknesses of the design of this study.

In this study the author noted the outcome of patients' illnesses and related them to whether he had adopted a 'positive' or a 'negative' approach to the patients' problems during the consultations, seeking to demonstrate whether or not a 'positive' approach would be helpful in speeding the patient's recovery. In doing so it was sometimes necessary for the doctor to vary his approach from that which he would 'naturally' have used in the circumstances.

The question asked about the design of the study presented because such a question might be asked of any similar study. The important features the examiners identified about it are shown in Table 10.2. A good answer would include those points, but simply to list them would not give a clear idea of how well the candidate understood them. For instance:

- Though the matter is an important one, it would strengthen the answer to say why the candidate thinks so. Is there other evidence that the relationship between the patient and the doctor is important and that the doctor's attitude is an active feature of the consultation?

- What is a randomized study, and why does that count as a strength? What would a good method of randomization be, and why should it be shown in the paper?

- Why does it matter that the study groups were not heterogeneous? To what extent does that reduce the value of the study? Though the endpoint is clearly stated, is that strength outweighed by the fact that it is subjective and therefore difficult to ensure consistency of recording? As far as the ambivalent features go, how dependable is a study that contains any such uncertainties?

Table 10.2 The principal features of a good answer to Example 10.2

The strengths

- It is an important area.
- It is relevant and reproducible.
- The hypothesis is clearly stated.
- It is a classical randomized intervention study.
- There is a clear endpoint (recovery at two weeks).

The weaknesses

- There is a possibility of selection bias.
- The study groups are not heterogeneous.
- Randomization method is not given.
- The 'negative consultation style' was not natural.
- The differences between 'negative' and 'positive' styles were not validated.
- Assessment of the endpoint (recovery) was very subjective.

Ambivalent features

- The single investigator lends consistency but reduces the ability to generalize; was the sample size adequate?

Example 10.3

Example 10.3 refers to an audit of the referral rates in a putative six-partner training practice:

Speculate on the possible reasons for the recorded outpatient referral rates of partner LS and the trainee in this six-partner training practice.

Prince Place Health Centre
Referrals per 100 consultations

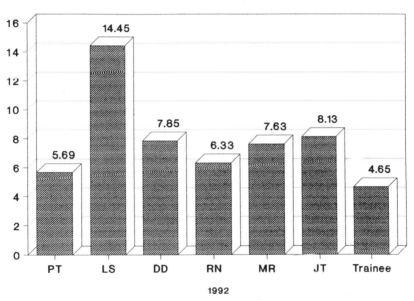

1992

The result showed that while five of the partners had similar rates one had a rate that was more than twice that of the lowest partner, and the trainee was the lowest of all. The question invited candidates to speculate on the reasons for the rates recorded by those two doctors.

The headings of the marking schedule used to mark this question are given in Table 10.3 and the reader is invited to consider how these headings might be expanded to give a fuller and better answer.

Further examples of recent CRQ paper questions are given in Appendix 8, and again the reader is invited to consider one or two

Table 10.3 The principal features of the marking schedule for Example 10.3

How valid is the exercise?

- Points to include are: sample size; length of collection period; whether there might be data collection faults; whether all referrals are included (some might be hand written, etc); when it was done (e.g. new doctor not seeing typical cases).

Doctor factors

- High rate might be caused by: personality, personal approach, burnout, lack of confidence, adverse experiences, workload, special interests, previous audits.

- Low rate might be caused by: referrals elsewhere (e.g. to Accident and Emergency), over-confidence, recent hospital experience.

Patient factors

- High rate might be caused by: older population, female, private patients, cross referrals.

- Low rate might be caused by: minor and acute illness, doctor–patient relationship, referral via other doctors.

An 'excellent' answer should identify all key themes and expand on them.

A 'satisfactory' answer should include: personality, experience, case-mix effects.

of these at leisure, and then to answer the remainder 'under examination conditions'.

The general approach to the CRQ should be similar to that in the MEQ.

- Take a calm and measured approach, reviewing the whole paper before writing the first answer.

- Think carefully about how the question is worded and phrased, and how that may indicate what lies behind the question.

- Take time to consider how the topic in question has featured in your reading and preparation, and how it has been encountered in your own experience.

- When starting the answer, make brief pencil notes on spare paper (e.g. inside the cover of the booklet, or even on the answer sheet) of the principal headings of the answer.

- Set out the answers clearly, tidily and legibly, using note form rather than long and discursive sentences.

The conclusion of the CRQ paper is also the end of the written part of the examination. Candidates then have a period of six weeks to wait, it is to be hoped not too anxiously, until the invitation to attend the orals is received by those whose results so far are sufficiently good to do so.

References

British Thoracic Society (1990) Guidelines for the management of asthma in adults: 1. Chronic persistent asthma. *British Medical Journal* **301**, 651–3.

Foulkes J (1992) Report to Examination Board, RCGP. Unpublished.

Thomas KB (1987) General practice consultations: is there any point in being positive? *British Medical Journal* **294**, 1200–2.

11 Approaching the Orals

Mention has already been made of the practice experience questionnaire (PEQ). This seeks information about the personal details of the candidate, and about the kind of practices he or she has worked in and the work that was done. The completed form must be returned to the Examination Department at the time of the written papers, or shortly afterwards. A final date for return is given on the questionnaire for each examination.

Practice experience questionnaire

The information sought in the PEQ is summarized in Table 11.1, and the whole form reproduced in Appendix 5. The candidates' personal details are self-explanatory but the purpose of this should be noted. The examiners need to know something of each candidate's personal circumstances in order to make their questions relevant to the individual's experience. A topic suitable for a trainee might be less searching for a principal, and vice versa. It is not that the more experienced doctor is expected to reach a higher standard but rather that the way the questions are put and followed up might differ in the two situations. While a trainee may make observations about a practice he has been working in he would not be expected to defend decisions made by others, but a principal should be able to justify the features of his or her own practice.

The sections on 'Practice structure' and 'Practice organization and facilities' give an indication of the kind of systems the candidate has experienced. The 'Workload analysis' shows how many patients have been seen by the candidate and other doctors in a typical recent week, as do the obstetric workload and the consulting rate.

Table 11.1 Information sought in the practice experience questionnaire

(A) Candidate's personal data

(B) Practice structure
List size and age structure
Number of doctors
Building and ownership, dispensing, training, fundholding
Urban or rural and any special features

(C) Practice organization and facilities
Personnel (nursing, paramedical, managerial, reception and clerical staff)
Whether staff are employed or attached
Minor surgery
Child health surveillance
Health promotion services
Chronic disease management clinics
Audit systems
Diagnostic, therapeutic and office equipment
How out-of-hours duties are covered

(D) Workload
Total attendances, attendance rates, obstetric activity

(E) The candidate's own ideas and learning experience
Stimulating and influential aspects of the candidate's work

(F) Clinical diary
25 cases seen in surgery
15 home visits
10 out-of-hours and emergency calls including two night visits

These three sections provide an opportunity to discuss aspects of practice management, practice policies and objectives, costs, priorities and any other matters germane to the organization of a general practice.

The 'Practice structure' section seeks information about the size of the practice list and its age and sex distribution, the number of doctors, the premises and who owns them, and features such as training, dispensing and fundholding. It also invites comments on any special features such as social or ethnic matters which might make it unusual and therefore of interest.

Under 'Practice organization and facilities' details of staffing and equipment are sought. Practices vary in size, staffing and facilities, and it may therefore be difficult for doctors in training to see the whole range of systems that exists. While it is incumbent upon candidates to know about the variety of staffing and equipment which exists in general, it is more discriminating to examine candidates on the services they have actually experienced, and can therefore describe and discuss from a practical rather than hypothetical point of view.

The questionnaire is only a means of gathering information on which the oral examiners can base their examination. It does not attract any marks in itself, nor is any information retrieved or stored by which to judge the practices described. The questionnaire is used only in the first oral, where it enables an assessment to be made of the candidate's ability to evaluate his working environment and the quality of care offered within it. In the case of young doctors particularly it allows the examiners to assess what the candidates have learned from their experiences. It is a document in which the candidate can indicate his or her ideas and activities, so it is worth taking trouble to prepare it and present it well.

Nevertheless, direct reference to the questionnaire forms only a small part of the examination and excessive time and effort should not be spent on preparation which might not be fruitful. Ideally it should be typed, though with modern wordprocessors being the norm now this is more difficult than it used to be! It is also sensible to keep a copy, not only of the questionnaire itself but more or less detailed notes of the cases listed. It is permissible to refer to this list in the examination when the cases are discussed.

Some candidates who have no recent experience of the full range of general practice activities such as night calls or clinics may find it difficult to complete a list of suitable cases; for instance, candidates doing locum or assistant work or who are on retainer schemes may not be doing night or emergency work, or doing few or no home visits. Wherever possible opportunities to do such work should be sought but if that is not possible the reason for omitting the appropriate entry should be given.

Objectives of the orals

The oral examinations provide an opportunity for the assessment of qualities different from those examined in the written papers. The papers are intended to assess the knowledge base (MCQ), the ability of candidates to use that knowledge appropriately in practical situations (MEQ), and the capacity to increase, modify and develop that knowledge and skill in a changing professional world (CRQ). Although the orals cover much the same ground in one way, in that they are based on current and important aspects of general practice, and introduce a clinical element in allowing discussion of actual cases, the qualities which are being examined and marked are not the same. The oral examination has an "immediacy and intimacy" which "allows judgements to be made of the candidate's approach to practice and the justification of that approach" (Tate et al., 1990). What is being assessed is the candidate's ability to identify and define problems, propose a range of rational courses of action, and justify those ideas and proposals in the face of critical challenge. The examiners look for evidence of a rational, coherent and consistent approach, based on good evidence which is identified or quoted, and is both justifiable and justified in the face of informed and reasonable challenge.

Areas of competence

In each oral the examiners must cover several topics in some detail, choosing them from a range of 'competences' in the various activities of general practice. In this way an overview of the candidate's approach to a variety of situations or problems is gained

101

which allows a general judgement to be reached. The examiners are not aware of the candidates' performance in the written examination at this stage; only after the orals are concluded and marks awarded are the results of the five sections combined and a decision reached as to whether a candidate is successful or not.

The seven areas of competence are shown in Table 11.2, together with the attributes which they contain. As they are set out these attributes could not be used as discriminating questions in the examination. Asking "What are your views on 'accessibility' or 'chronic disease'?" would be meaningless and impossible to mark. To convert these concepts into markable and discriminating questions which can be used in the oral examination the examiners choose clinical or other situations which have, or might have, arisen in practice and which illustrate the concepts contained in the seven areas of competence. Some areas, such as 'Practice organization', fall more suitably into the first oral, whereas others, such as 'Professional values', fit more easily into the second, but the intention is to cover as many of the areas as possible in each.

In practice, as time is limited to 30 minutes and each area needs 5 minutes or so to examine adequately, usually only five or six areas are covered. At the end of the first oral a note of the topics discussed is passed from the first to the second examiner pair, so that although the area of competence will probably be tested again a different approach will be used. Examples of how questions are constructed under each heading, and how appropriate answers may be developed will be given in Chapters 12 and 13.

Marking the orals

Having asked the question, received answers, and taken the discussion as far as necessary to make a judgement (or as far as time will allow if judgement proves elusive) the examiners must award a mark. Each question is marked separately as the examination proceeds but the final mark is not a mathematical sum of those marks. At the end of the oral each examiner reflects on the overall performance of the candidate, and using the marks for each question and his or her own impression of the candidate's performance overall, gives a total mark which reflects that

Table 11.2 The seven areas of competence assessed in the orals, and the attributes they contain

- **Problem definition**
  Application of knowledge
  Recognizing the whole problem
  Applying probabilities
  Considering options
  Critical thinking

- **Management**
  Whole patient care
  Life-threatening problems
  Chronic disease
  Psychological problems
  Use of resources
  Prescribing

- **Prevention**
  Preventive medicine
  Health education

- **Practice organization**
  Accessibility
  Teamwork
  Time management
  Priorities

- **Communication**
  Doctor–patient communication
  Patients' health beliefs

- **Professional values**
  Respect for life
  Responsibility and reliability
  Respect for people
  Empathy and sensitivity
  Integrity and ethics
  Enjoyment and enthusiasm

- **Personal and professional growth**
  Self-awareness
  Personal/professional balances
  Self-assessment
  Reading and literature
  Continuing education

evidence. The examiners do not confer and do not need to agree on the mark, though only infrequently do the overall marks differ greatly.

Scale of categories

The marks are chosen from a scale of descriptions depicting various qualities of performance, shown in Table 11.3. In coming to a decision about a candidate's answer the examiners do not ask: "Was the answer right or wrong?", nor even "How much does the candidate know about this subject?" Indeed the questions asked in the orals often do not have a 'correct' answer because they deal with dilemmas, paradoxes and controversial issues that may be faced in day-to-day practice. Rather, they ask themselves: "How well does the candidate understand the implications of the situation presented, and of proposed responses? How good is the evidence he or she gives for the stated beliefs or behaviours? How appropriate are the influences the candidate declares? Is there evidence of consistency and justifiable decision-making? Does the candidate actually do what he says he does? How rigid or flexible is this candidate in her views or her approach to a situation? Can the candidate see both sides of an argument and make a reasoned and

---

Table 11.3 The categories of marks used in the orals

- Outstanding
- Excellent
- Good
- Satisfactory
- Bare pass

- Not very good
- Unsatisfactory
- Poor
- Dangerous

---

tenable decision between them?" On the basis of the answers to these questions they find a description from the scale of categories which best fits their opinion of the candidate's performance. That is then entered on the marking sheet as a letter symbolizing the chosen grade.

The very best category which a candidate can achieve is graded 'Outstanding'. Such a candidate is characterized by a consistently good performance which shows evidence of wide reading and is coherent, rational and critical. The approaches given are spontaneously justified by reference to the relevant literature. Such a mark is rarely given, perhaps to 1% or 2% of candidates. 'Excellent', reached by perhaps 5% to 10%, shows the same qualities as the outstanding candidate but is not quite so uniformly good, although clearly impressive and very competent. To achieve 'Good' the candidate would need to be well-informed and able to present policies coherently and critically but would not demonstrate the degree of confidence and competence to justify a higher grade. The ability to make decisions would be good, and most of them would be well justified, though perhaps without so much spontaneous and confident reference to the literature. The grade of 'Satisfactory' is given when answers are mostly well-reasoned and sensible, if inconsistent at times, and though they may be justifiable the candidate cannot always be convincing. The decision-making skills are adequate rather than good, and the candidate appears secure and reasonably competent if not sparkling.

'Bare pass' is just enough to allow a candidate to pass if all the other marks are adequate, but would not compensate for a low mark in the papers. It is given when an examiner feels that the candidate is only just good enough, and although decisions and policies are usually sensible there is little or no ability to justify them. Though the skills of making decisions or proposing a range of options are, on balance, acceptable they are not consistent or secure.

Below this level the candidate is unlikely to pass the examination overall unless the papers achieved high marks. 'Not very good', as it suggests, is applied to a candidate who gives questionable answers and is unable to say why a particular course of action was proposed, or why it might be appropriate. The basic knowledge of topics covered in the oral seems scanty or is not well applied. The ability to make decisions is poor, even to the extent of being potentially risky in practice. 'Unsatisfactory' describes a candidate who is often inconsistent, who cannot, or only rarely can, support decisions with reasons or evidence. Such a candidate would not seem to be capable of passing the examination overall, though may have done well enough to reach an oral. If the grade 'Poor' is given, it signifies that the examiners have seen some scanty evidence of ability but not enough to justify passing the candidate because the approach to practice is so inconsistent and incoherent. Such a candidate is quite unable to justify any of the answers given or decisions made, which are sometimes not even justifiable.

The lowest category of all is 'Dangerous'. This would be given to a candidate who was so ignorant of important matters as to put patients at risk, or who knowingly and deliberately proposed actions which were hazardous, improper or illegal. Fortunately candidates rarely, if ever, put examiners in the position of having to describe them as dangerous, but the grade is included to safeguard the College from admitting someone who professed such ideas.

At the end of the orals the letter symbols by which the examiners have indicated their judgements are entered into the computer, which converts them to a mathematical mark. This is then added to the marks gained in the other oral and the written examination, each section contributing an equal amount. At the conclusion of all the orals the total marks of the individual candidates are placed in rank order, expressed as a percentage of the total marks available. Those who have gained 50% or more are deemed to have passed the examination, and have become Members of the Royal College of General Practitioners.

Reference

Tate P, Tombleson PJ and Southgate L (1990) Present state and future developments. In *Examination for Membership of the Royal College of General Practitioners (MRCGP). Occasional Paper 46.* Ed. Lockie C. London, Royal College of General Practitioners. pp 30–4.

12 Taking the First Oral

Candidates may be forgiven for expecting the oral part of the examination to be stressful because it consists of direct face-to-face challenges. It need not be so, however, because adequate preparation based on an understanding of the oral process and objectives will enable a confident and assured approach to be made. Furthermore, the examiners, who are all experienced and practising general practitioners themselves, approach the task in a constructive and positive manner rather than negatively searching for some way to 'fail' the candidates. Their task is to provide opportunities for the candidates to show their qualities and to award marks accordingly, so it is up to the candidates to take those opportunities.

Candidates should approach the orals in a similar way, that is to say openly, positively and constructively. In the terminology of transactional analysis, this is an adult-to-adult transaction (Berne, 1974). The examiners try to use every moment to good effect and, although wishing to provide time for the candidate to relax and have space in which to think and formulate ideas, they will move on to new topics as soon as they have formed a judgement in a particular area. Candidates should not feel put out if the subject changes abruptly or if they are stopped in full flood just as they warm to their task. It does not indicate that they have not given the 'right' answer or that they have missed the point, but rather that the examiners have formed their judgement and wish to move to another area where the candidate can continue to demonstrate his or her qualities.

Each part of the oral is intended to cover five or six of the areas of competence. To illustrate how that may be done, an example from each area will be taken and some approaches to answering them outlined; how the examiners make their judgements will then be described. There is no real distinction between the manner of presentation in the two parts of the orals, but for the purpose of illustration this chapter will deal with examples such as might come from the first oral based on the practice experience questionnaire. The next chapter will deal with the second oral.

The first oral

The candidate is shown to the appropriate table, where the examiners introduce themselves and invite the candidate to sit down and feel at ease. The examination is conducted in a relaxed and conversational manner, although of course the tasks of assessment and forming a judgement must be addressed. There may be one or two remarks to clarify some point of identity or about the practice experience questionnaire, but usually the first question is put very soon. Normally the examiner who starts the question follows it through to its conclusion and forms a judgement, while the other assesses the answers and also awards a mark. Sometimes, however, the co-examiner will join in the discussion either to clarify a point, to help the candidate to expand somewhat where that would be helpful, or to challenge or develop something that has been said. Such interaction is usually helpful, and is often made specifically to enable the candidate to gain a better mark.

Usually the topic will be opened up with a general remark which introduces the area to be examined and gives the candidate a brief time to marshal thoughts about it. It also gives the examiner a feel for the candidate's competence, though at this stage it is probably not enough to form a 'markable' judgement. Then the crux of the question is presented, which usually exposes some paradox or dilemma which the candidate is invited to discuss. He or she may be asked to propose various courses of action; to speculate on possible causes for a presentation described; or to describe his or her attitude to a controversial issue. It is not the 'correctness' of the answer which gains marks but the way in which the topic is discussed, how well the arguments for or against are supported with evidence, how well the decisions are made and why, and how well the implications of those decisions are understood. Thus it is often the case that a candidate has given a good answer and has taken it as far as possible but the examiner sees some opportunity to reveal a greater competence and will therefore push the candidate a bit harder. At this point some candidates might feel that they are unable to go further and that therefore they have lost marks. In fact the examiner is giving them an opportunity to do better and is considering whether a higher mark could be given. In such a situation candidates should not feel they have not done well for they may indeed have been doing better than they expected.

Based as they are on the practice experience questionnaire, the questions in the first oral are drawn from the material which the candidates present in the questionnaire. The examiners must select topics from this which cover most of the seven areas of competence. They will have read the PEQ beforehand and selected some suitable topics. A typical first oral might proceed as follows.

Example 12.1

As the questionnaire features practice details before the candidate's own ideas and the case diary, it is often a 'Practice organization' question that comes first. For instance, the PEQ might show that the practice employs three part-time nurses. The candidate is invited to outline the duties of the nurses in this practice, which helps to establish a common ground for discussion but would probably not generate any actual marks. The discussion would therefore be brief and would lead on to a variety of questions, such as:

- What factors would a practice need to consider when appointing a new nurse?
- What are the candidate's views about nurse-run disease management clinics?
- How would the doctors satisfy themselves that the nurses were fulfilling their duties to an adequate standard?
- What might they do if they felt it was inadequate?

This topic has been chosen as a result of the candidate having mentioned it in the PEQ. Similarly if the practice employed a physiotherapist, ran a travel clinic or lent relaxation tapes to patients, this would indicate to the examiners that these were within the candidate's experience. The candidate should therefore know something about the topic and be able to discuss it from an informed position. It is vital therefore that if something is mentioned in the PEQ the candidate should be prepared to talk about it, the significant word being 'prepared'. The corollary is that if he or she is not prepared to talk about it, it should not be mentioned in the PEQ.

The marks in Example 12.1 will be awarded for the candidate's ability to discuss the matter sensibly, to give a balanced account of the responsibilities of employers generally and of employing another professional worker in particular; no attempt is made to examine or justify what actually happens in the practice which the PEQ describes. In this question a candidate might be given a 'Satisfactory' mark if he could give a clear indication that he understood the duties of the practice nurse, namely that she was a professional in her own right but operating within the discipline of the practice, that he was familiar with the nursing staff grading and remuneration system, and that he understood the legal responsibilities of employers. To achieve 'Good' he would have to show a more detailed understanding of the legal situation or give a job description, and perhaps describe a continuous practice audit system to cover the nursing department. To gain 'Excellent' this would need to be given with confidence and reference to the rules of employment in the NHS (Red Book) and relevant legislation.

Example 12.2

The next area that attracts the examiners' attention might be that the practice has been accepted at Band 3 for health promotion. This topic might be examined under several of the areas of competence (see Table 11.2). Although it clearly involves practice organization this has been covered in the first question. It is also relevant to:

- **Prevention:** Does taking people's blood pressure prevent disease? If so how do you know what you have prevented? Where is the evidence to support your statements? What does it cost, and is it cost effective? If not, how could the money be spent better?

- **Communication:** How does the practice persuade patients to take up the service offered? Who accepts? Do the people who need it most get it most? How do you 'promote health'? How do you know when you have done it? What do the patients think about it, and does it change their beliefs?

- **Professional values:** Is general practice the best place to 'promote health'? Could other people and other systems be used to better effect? Should not doctors be curing illness, which is what they are trained to do? Is the financial reward in Band 3 adequate for the work done and the staff employed to do it? Where does that money actually come from?

Which area of competence is eventually examined depends to some extent on how the candidate responds. If he volunteers an enthusiastic response to the idea of improving the health of the practice population by education, by reaching the parts that other systems do not, by the employment of a dietitian and a stop-smoking counsellor, it might count as 'Communication' or perhaps 'Professional values'. If he professes the belief that screening for hypercholesterolaemia, hypertension or glycosuria is the key to prevention of disease, it would probably be taken under 'Prevention'. This is not important to the candidate in one sense, because in either case marks will be awarded on the quality of the answer, and the area will have to be covered in some way. On the other hand the candidate chooses the answers and expresses his attitude and the degree of enthusiasm with which he holds it. In doing so he contributes to the direction of the examination and influences the way in which the examiners conduct it. It is therefore important that he is positive in response and chooses answers which keep him in areas in which he is confident whenever possible.

Example 12.3

The area of 'Personal and professional growth' might seem somewhat abstruse or remote from the immediate task of passing the examination but actually it is central to it. The whole business of training for general practice is about producing good doctors who have the necessary knowledge and skills, who have desirable attitudes, and who are people whose personalities can tolerate the demands and pressures of a responsible profession. It is therefore entirely germane to the examination. The question the examiners are asking is: "How does this candidate deal with the need to grow and develop professionally, both now and in the future?"

A candidate may have stated in his PEQ that he has carried out an audit of some part of the practice's work, or that some aspect of the practice excited him and developed his ideas. The examiners would be interested to know why the subject of the audit was chosen, what was learned, and how that learning was used; or what excited the candidate and why, and how this altered his attitude to his work. The candidate will be asked to describe the matter briefly to open the discussion. The word 'briefly' will be emphasized because the examiners will not want to spend time on describing the project itself. Such a description would not be markable as they would not be able to corroborate statements made; it would be 'hearsay' and therefore not evidence. What they want to know is what the candidate has learned from the exercise, how his beliefs and understanding have changed, how this has been adopted in his work, whether he has read other material on the same topic and whether that supported or conflicted with his own findings. It is also of interest to know whether he has shared his findings with others, whether the audit result indicated a need for changed behaviour not only with him but with other doctors or other workers in the practice. If so, how was this need addressed and received? How does he deal with controversy and conflict?

A candidate who demonstrated familiarity with the principles of audit and who described how he conceived, designed and implemented his own audit and acted upon the findings might achieve 'Satisfactory' or 'Good', depending on the clarity and consistency of his description. One who was able to put the idea in the context of other work in the same field, to summarize the issues underlying the choice of subject, and to answer critical challenges with spontaneously quoted evidence from the literature or his own proven work would be in line for 'Excellent' or even 'Outstanding'. On the other hand, if he were unable to show good reasons for the audit, merely doing it because it was required of him; or if he claimed to be, but patently was not excited by the aspect of the practice he mentioned; or could not show that this had taught anything of value to him or anyone else, he is not going to convince the examiners that he justifies more than a 'Bare pass', or worse still a 'Not very good'.

The lesson here is that when deciding how to complete the section of the PEQ on the candidate's own ideas and learning experience it is essential to mention those things which really have moved you in the course of training, and to answer them with conviction and enthusiasm. If nothing has excited you about it, more is the pity, but it is important not to reveal that omission. It is to be hoped, however, that something has stimulated you. This is your chance to show your personal qualities of enthusiasm and interest, and it is specifically included to provide such an opportunity for individual performance.

Three areas of competence have now been examined and probably half the time allowed has elapsed. Usually the examiners turn to the case diary at this point, though sometimes they choose to start with it. In the oral being described here the examiners will now note that they have not yet touched on the areas of 'Problem definition', 'Management' and 'Communication', so will choose cases from the diary which will be able to take them in to these areas.

Example 12.4

The candidate's case diary contains the following entry:

5/3/94 Joan B. Female 52 yrs. Blood pressure check. Follow-up.

The examiner will ask for a brief outline of the presentation; by brief is meant one or two short sentences, for no marks will be awarded for this and time would be wasted on a long exposition of the case. The examiner chooses to look at 'Management' and asks a question such as: "What are your objectives in a situation like this?" Note that the question is not specific to this case—"What did you do?", but "In cases like this what are you intending to do?" The question was a very open one and answers to it will give a good idea of the range of the candidate's competence; that is, his underlying views on the subject, his attitudes to benefits and difficulties of treating hypertension, how he relates to the patients he is looking after, his understanding of the patients' own attitudes to it and so on. There may not yet be a clear idea of the candidate's ability in this area, so the examiner may go deeper into the subject, choosing lines of approach such as:

113

- How well does he understand the indications and contraindications of the treatment?

- Does he have a range of therapies and is he able to justify why he uses one rather than another?

- Is he able to discover what the patients think about their condition and their treatment?

- Does he understand the costs and benefits of his actions in the short and long term, both to the patients and to society?

- Can he discuss the implications for the practice of having many or few patients who need follow-up and repeat prescriptions?

Behind these questions there lies the content of the 'Management' area of competence (see Table 11.2). The examiner will be looking for evidence that the candidate has a demonstrable understanding of the following aspects of managing the care of patients like this in the long term:

- That this is a matter that relates to the whole patient, not just the medication

- That there are, albeit rarely, life-threatening considerations

- That this is a long-term programme

- That there is a psychological component to the care of patients like this one, and that the patient and doctor must be able to communicate and understand each other

- That this subject has implications for the careful use of resources of personnel and money

- That knowledge and competence in selecting the best medication and delivery system are important.

In short, this is not a question about the treatment of raised blood pressure but about the management of a case in all its aspects over a long period of time.

If the candidate can demonstrate a familiarity with and competence in the main issues outlined above, it would probably ensure 'Satisfactory' or 'Good', depending on the degree of confidence with which it was given. To get a better mark would require that he was able to do so in relation to the major studies published on the matter, and to mention the inherent paradoxes (for example, the large number of people who have to take the medicine to prevent one stroke) and to take a view which was based on a balance of evidence. The candidate who merely does what appears right without knowing why, who does not regard the patient's view, who is rigid in attitude and limited in knowledge and who does not understand the implications of his decisions will not do so well, probably heading for a 'Not very good', or even 'Poor'. Marks are awarded in relation to what is expected of any candidate in this examination rather than against a checklist of required answers. In the situation described above the candidate himself had entered the case in the PEQ, so preparation of the subject was essential as it was very likely to be chosen.

There may now be 8 to 10 minutes left for this oral, and the examiners will have begun to form an idea of the final mark. Is the candidate doing well? Is he well read, able to make good decisions, be flexible when necessary but firm if needed? Does he need to be given a chance to improve his mark with more demanding challenges? Or is he floundering, not revealing the ability that seems to be there but which he cannot demonstrate? They also have to consider whether they have covered all the areas of competence adequately, and if not what has been omitted. They would find that, in the examples given here, 'Communication' and 'Problem definition' have not really been adequately tested, and will look for cases where this can be done. If the candidate is clearly very good they will choose questions that test him in difficult areas giving him the chance to score highly but not penalizing him with bad marks if he does not do as well as they thought he might. If he is not so good, and it is difficult to be sure whether he is 'Bare pass' or 'Satisfactory' they may go back to a straightforward clinical question which ought to be within everyone's competence. Examples of how these different strategies might work are given below, using the more straightforward one first.

Example 12.5

A case diary entry says:

5/3/94 John T. Male 42 years. Abdominal pain.

The candidate is asked to outline the case, again briefly. He describes the presentation of a man on a Monday morning with a history of two days' central abdominal pain and some nausea but no diarrhoea, and similar episodes in the past. The examiner might stop him there and ask what ideas are in his mind at that point in the consultation; in other words, does the candidate begin to form a strategy to address the problem as it presents to him? Or he might wait until the case has been more fully detailed and then ask how the candidate decided to proceed with it and what other options he had considered. Either way the candidate is being asked to demonstrate his working methods, so that the examiner can form judgements about how well he applies the knowledge he displays to the problem in hand, and whether he recognizes aspects of the problem that are not openly declared. For instance:

- Does he give a ready account of likely reasons for the presentation and possible causes?

- Does he spontaneously quote the possibility of a hidden agenda on the Monday morning?

- Does he recognize social factors such as family matters, employment and unemployment, smoking and alcohol consumption in causing presentations like this one?

If the examiner's suspicion that this candidate is not doing very well is proving true, time may be spent on teasing out these areas, addressing the task of assessing the candidate's competence in the area of 'Problem definition'. A few minutes might be allowed for the candidate to cover limited ground as well as he can, being guided by the examiners in revealing abilities which seem to be there but which he has not organized satisfactorily and does not display well. Or it might seem that he has recognized the problem quite well, and the examiner wants to know how he deals with it. From the list of possible causes for the presentation can the candidate suggest the most likely in the circumstances? What can he do to confirm his opinion? What investigations should he do, if any, and how will they help? Are there any benefits or disadvantages in investigation at this stage, and if so to whom? What options are there for managing the problem that has been presented? How will he choose between them, and why? (Is Monday morning surgery a good time to tackle someone about his excessive alcohol consumption?) Is what he says he would do consistent with other things he has said in this interview, and with his professed beliefs?

If, on the other hand the candidate has been doing very well he may be in the running for 'Excellent' or even 'Outstanding', in which case the examiners will want to offer the chance to show those qualities. It might be done as follows.

Example 12.6

11/2/94 William J. Male, aged 41. Depression, threatening suicide. Night visit.

This is a demanding situation for even the most competent of doctors. Life is in danger (maybe even the doctor's), there is no help at hand in the night, the doctor is under stress himself ... It might not be necessary to ask the candidate to describe the scene any further, for the five words in the case diary set the scene very clearly. The examiners still have not fully examined this candidate in the area of 'Communication', and to do so they might ask themselves:

- How does he relate to the patient in circumstances like this?

- Can he adapt his methods of consultation to suit these circumstances?

- How does he judge the patient's mood, assess his intentions and the likelihood of suicide?

- How much does he allow the patient to take responsibility for his own decisions and actions?

- How has he developed the strategies which he describes?

- How does he adapt the models of consultation he may have read about to a situation like this one?

- Is he aware of recent initiatives in the field of depression, and from what authorities?

- Could he name a book or paper which has formed or changed his thinking on depressive illness, and in what way did it do so?

At this point, to everyone's relief, a bell or gong will be sounded to indicate that the half-hour is finished, and the candidates will leave the examination hall for a few minutes' relaxation and relief. The examiners, however, will have to reflect upon their notes and come individually to a final mark. This is then passed to the examination administrator to add to the totals as they accumulate, but it is not passed to the second pair of examiners, who will therefore meet the candidate without bias from such information. Five to 10 minutes' interval is allowed for this before the candidates return to meet the second pair of examiners, and enter the final phase of the examination.

Reference

Berne E (1974) *What Do You Say After You've Said Hello?* London, Andre Deutsch.

13 Taking the Second Oral

The candidates return to the examination hall after the break, but to different tables and other examiners. Let us imagine that the candidate in these examples is female, for half of the candidates in recent examinations are women. As before, the examiners stand to introduce themselves and identify the new candidate, and once re-seated start the examination without delay. They will have been given a list of topics covered in the first oral and will avoid repeating them, but of course they have the same task of covering the seven areas of competence using different topics to do so.

The first topic to be chosen is likely to be a straightforward one and will probably follow the usual pattern of a brief exposition of the topic leading to more detailed and penetrating questions which explore the candidate's competence more deeply. The examples given here are taken from those used by the author, and suggest some of the responses which candidates have given as well as those which were sought.

Example 13.1

In the following example the examiner is assessing the candidate's ability in the area of 'Problem definition'. It has been chosen because it deals with a common and significant clinical problem, namely loss of weight, and offers the candidate the opportunity to show her basic problem-solving skills in a clinical situation. The examiners are looking for answers to questions like:

- How well does she apply the basic knowledge to the situation as it is presented to her?
- How well does she recognize the problem facing the patient as a whole rather than the presenting symptom alone?

- How well does she consider the probable causes in relation to the possible causes?

- How good are the ideas she proposes for discussion with the patient?

The examiner starts with a broad question to enable the candidate to think herself into the situation, such as "When a middle-aged patient comes to you complaining of weight loss, what likely causes do you consider?" In response, a competent candidate would quickly indicate several of the most likely such as diabetes, neoplasm, thyrotoxicosis and gastro-intestinal disease, and suggest some less probable conditions such as tuberculosis and psychological factors to show that she is aware that uncommon things do occur in general practice. Then the question becomes more specific. The examiner outlines the case of a man aged 55 who was previously fit but has lost five kilograms in weight and complains of feeling very tired; he asks: "What further information do you need and what tests or investigations might you consider to help you reach a diagnosis?"

The examiner is looking for evidence that the candidate is able to proceed logically and rationally through a process of gathering information from the patient to amplify what is already known, and to formulate a plan for investigation that suits the case and do so in the circumstances of general practice.

- How well does she assess the severity of the case, the probability of one rather than another of the differential diagnoses, and choose investigations that are appropriate?

- How well does she use the resources that are available in terms of cost, benefit and relevance?

- How well does she show that she can pursue the probable without ignoring the improbable?

- How well does she consider the options open to her and choose between them rationally and for good reasons?

Most candidates should be able to give a confident and clear outline of how they would proceed in such a situation, and would be marked 'Satisfactory' or 'Good', depending on the confidence and competence they showed. It is unlikely to generate higher marks than that because it examines basic problem-solving skills and is not looking for unusual abilities. However not all candidates can show that they have a confident familiarity with such a situation, that they can make rational and sensible decisions in the context of a real general practice consultation. They may have knowledge but not be able to apply it relevantly, or be extravagant in the use of resources because they are not using them rationally. Such candidates would achieve a 'Bare pass' or less.

Example 13.2

The other examiner, having been listening to and marking the first question, now has her turn (for many, though not enough, examiners are women). She decides to examine in the area of 'Prevention' and asks the candidate what she understands by the word 'screening'. This is an open question introducing a new topic, so the candidate might well take a moment or two to collect her thoughts. She could ask herself where this question is going to lead and what might lie behind it. It is better to do that than give a hasty unprepared response; indeed it might enhance the examiner's opinion to see that she reflects properly upon the question. Defining screening as the attempt to detect disease before symptoms occur would be satisfactory, but if she spontaneously described Wilson's criteria (1965), and better still said when and why the criteria were defined, she might show the examiners that she was 'Good' or even 'Excellent', and they would begin to look for evidence to support that possibility—in which case the questions might seem to become 'harder'. The point here is that if the examination appears to be getting difficult it may be because the candidate is doing well and is being offered the opportunity to show that she justifies a high mark, and not just that she does not know the answer. Examiners sometimes push candidates as far as they can to discover whether they are 'Excellent' or 'Outstanding', and if the candidate 'dries up' at this stage she may still have achieved a better mark than if the questions had been easier.

To probe deeper the examiner might now ask the candidate to compare the cervical cytology and the mammography screening programmes and say how well they meet Wilson's criteria. This would expose the good candidate to the challenge of two topics at the same time, and demand that she reveal her views not only on whether the programmes do meet the criteria but also how well each of them does so in comparison with the other. To do so fluently and concisely would show considerable ability. An easier way of testing on this point would be to ask about one programme only, but it might be more difficult to achieve a high mark in the simpler question. The examiners will form their judgement according to how well they think she has:

- Shown the strengths of each programme, such as the reduction in mortality that they can achieve

- Exposed the weaknesses of either programme, such as whether they really do detect presymptomatic disease

- Compared the costs with the benefits, not only in terms of money and resources but also from the patients' and society's point of view

- Given the sources of her information from reading such as the Forrest Report (1986), experience such as a study she has carried out personally, and reflection upon those

- Formed a judgement about them which is her own and which she can defend and justify.

A candidate who cannot give such responses, or whose answers are inconsistent and irrational, or who accepts that these things are here and is unable to form a critical view is likely to get a 'Bare pass' or 'Not very good'. However, let us follow our present candidate in another question.

Many examiners will form their questions around a topic which has achieved prominence in the press, either in the medical journals or the public domain. For instance, there have been articles, papers and correspondence about whether it is right to deny treatment to patients while they continue to smoke tobacco. There is no 'correct' answer to this, but it is surely an area which a general practitioner should be able to discuss with confidence and insight. The question might be disguised, albeit thinly, in an everyday clinical situation, as in the following example.

Example 13.3

The examiner outlines a case thus:

A patient comes to your surgery and tells you that her husband, whom you had referred to a cardiovascular surgeon for probable coronary artery bypass graft, has been refused treatment because he is a heavy smoker. She appears distressed and angry. How might you respond to a presentation like this?

The candidate would do well to reflect on this for a moment, and consider what lies behind the question. Is it about coronary artery surgery? Probably not. Or is it about consultation and communication? Probably not. It is a clinical situation in which the professional values of the doctor individually and her colleagues in the hospital are being challenged. There are various other aspects to the situation which might well be interesting questions, such as dealing through a 'third party' and the problem of what to do about the husband's illness, but these will not be pursued in this instance. The examiner wants to know what view the candidate takes about the allegation that doctors withhold treatment from some patients, how that view has been formed and whether it can be justified. In giving her answer a good candidate might include ideas such as:

- Is what the wife says entirely accurate? Has the surgeon really 'refused treatment'?

- Life is not prolonged by surgery in patients who smoke, though symptoms may be relieved.

- There is a valid case for the view that everyone is entitled to the treatment they need and smokers pay heavily for it in tax on their tobacco.

- There are other groups of people who might seem to justify the withholding of treatment such as alcohol and drug abusers and those who deliberately take overdoses, but this is not done.

- Show how she would explain her own position to the patient and his wife, and that cessation of smoking is in itself a treatment for his disease.

- Refer to the debate in the *British Medical Journal* (Underwood et al., 1993) and elsewhere.

123

This is a topic which could be discussed at length but the examiners must bring it to an end as soon as they have formed a judgement. The mark awarded will depend on how well the candidate has made out the case for the attitude she adopts, not on the attitude itself, which might be the opposite of the examiner's. The candidate who holds no view, who has not given it any thought or even read about it, will not do well; those who are rational, consistent and well informed will.

It is necessary to move on to another area because the examination's reliability depends on testing as many samples of the candidate's competence as possible. The other examiner now takes over and wishes to look at the candidate's competence in the area of 'Practice organization', which has not yet been done in this oral. This question originated in a comment in the *British Medical Journal* that general practitioners were not adequately conversant with their responsibilities under the Health and Safety legislation. It also provides an opportunity to consider competence in non-clinical areas which are the responsibility of doctors who are also employers.

Example 13.4

The topic is introduced with a broad and open question inviting the candidate to list some of the legislation and regulations which affect the organization of general practice. The list might include such things as the National Health Service Acts, the Medicines Act, Misuse of Drugs regulations, the Children's Act, the Mental Health Act, and the one which the examiner is looking for, namely the Health and Safety at Work Act, and the Control of Substances Hazardous to Health regulations (COSHH). Little or no marks will be awarded for this list in itself, but in a few moments the examiner will have formed an idea of how confident the candidate is in this area. Then the examiner becomes more specific, declaring Health and Safety as the area to be examined and asking what a general practitioner's responsibilities are under this legislation. A satisfactory answer to this part of the question would include:

- The purpose of the law, to ensure that all who work in or visit the practice premises are not exposed to unreasonable hazards to their health

- Some specific examples of possible hazards such as infections, poisoning or risks from defective premises or equipment

- The requirement to make an assessment of all the hazards and risks in the areas for which the practice is responsible

- The difference between a hazard (the potential to cause harm) and a risk (the probability that harm will occur)

- That equipment, both medical and non-medical, must be checked regularly for safety

- Mention of some substances that come under COSHH regulations

- What the employer must do to ensure risk is minimized to everyone, including staff, patients and other visitors.

On the face of it this question and the answers outlined might seem to deal in factual knowledge, which is the province of the MCQ. It is of interest to the examiner that the facts should be given correctly, but it is not the ability to list the facts but to use them which is being tested. In this area of 'Practice organization' the examiner is assessing to what extent the candidate accepts the legal responsibilities of being an employer, and how well she could organize the various members of practice staff to comply with those responsibilities. To do so in greater depth the examiner might ask her to describe how she would make an assessment under the COSHH regulations.

A 'Satisfactory' answer would be that she would: "Go through all the rooms in the building and make a list of everything that could possibly be harmful, and tell everybody to be careful about them; also keep them out of the way of patients, including children." To be 'Good' or 'Excellent' would require that she discuss the intended assessment at a practice meeting; decide policy about which partner is responsible for it; which staff member or members will assist with it or have it delegated to them; how the assessment will be reported to the partners; whether and how dangerous substances might be removed and substituted; and how everyone, both partners and staff, will be informed about it all. To be able to do all this concisely and confidently in a few sentences would indicate considerable competence in leading a team, which is one

125

of the attributes specified in the area of 'Practice organization'. Given the large expansion in practice premises and equipment, the publicity recently given to standards of practice and the consequences of failure to comply with this legislation, a candidate who was unable to show minimum competence would risk 'Unsatisfactory' or even 'Poor', which are very low marks.

The other examiner, meanwhile, though listening to and assessing the candidate's performance, is considering what areas have not yet been examined. He finds that 'Communication', 'Management', and 'Personal and professional growth' remain, but there is time for only two more topics. So he chooses a question which can cover both 'Communication' and 'Management', and having a competent candidate with them at present believes that both may be assessed under the same topic, and briefly outlines a case similar to one which occurred in his own practice.

Example 13.5

You are just coming to the end of morning surgery, rather behind time and have many things to do that morning. Your next patient, who you believe to be the last, is a 50-year-old man who you expect to be coming as a follow up of some minor surgery you did last week. You are therefore somewhat surprised when he comes in with his wife, both of them looking very gloomy and unhappy. How might you proceed with this unexpected situation?

On the face of it this is a problem-solving question, but the examiner is only using this scene-setting as a way of getting quickly to the area he wishes to examine in a realistic rather than a theoretical way. It puts it dynamically as opposed to an arid: "How do you cope with the unexpected?" In the process he can see how well the candidate responds to the changed situation, and how versatile and flexible her approach can be. It will also enable him to phrase his next question according to her response; if it is competent he will proceed rapidly to the heart of the matter; if hesitant he will go more slowly, testing for basic competence rather than excellence.

He then describes how the husband and wife told him that they had a stormy argument with their 21-year-old son who then left home to live in a homosexual relationship with a man twice his age.

Furthermore they believe that the older man is HIV-positive, which they had heard on the grapevine. They believe him to be a very unpleasant person.

The purpose of this question is to assess several aspects of the candidate's competence.

- How well can she relate to people who are distressed and anxious?

- How well does she cope with the conflict between pressures on her own time and the need to give enough time to this new development?

- How good is her understanding of the way people form their health beliefs, and how doctors and others can modify them?

- Does she have a repertoire of consultation methods which is flexible and adaptable to various circumstances?

- Where did she learn these methods, and has she adapted them to suit her own style and needs?

- How well does she hear what these people are saying and formulate a range of ideas to help them?

- How good is she at communicating those ideas to the patients and knowing that they understand and whether they agree?

Answers to this question are not judged on what the candidate would do in this case which is, after all, hypothetical as presented in the examination. The grade of mark depends on the variety of ideas which she displays, the quality of the reasons which she gives to support her proposals and her understanding of the implications of what she says and does. Even then it is not sufficient merely to give a list of possible actions; it is necessary to be able to make sensible and acceptable decisions.

With the oral entering its last few minutes the area of 'Personal and professional growth' remains untested. The final topic is therefore introduced, and as the candidate seems to be doing well she is challenged with what some candidates might feel is a threatening problem. Good candidates have a chance to enhance their marks from such a question, but the less able need not fear that there is some cryptic or hidden trick. They will not be marked severely if they do not do well, but in accordance with how others would be expected to answer. Weak candidates would probably not be asked such a question.

Example 13.6

The examiner introduces this topic with a disarmingly short and direct question: "What is a Service Committee in the NHS?" If the candidate replies correctly so much the better, but if not, she will not lose marks. She then invites the candidate to imagine that she is now a partner in a practice and a complaint is made to the FHSA. It is alleged that there was a delay in answering a request for a visit to a sick child, the doctor who visited did not recognize the problem, which further delayed the child's admission to hospital with suspected meningitis. The complaint is upheld, the doctor is penalized, and everyone feels very unhappy and distressed about it. What can be done to learn from such an adverse experience?

This question is about the candidate's personal ability to learn and to develop her professional stature. Given the increasing complexity of medicine, the increase in stress perceived by many general practitioners and the need to demonstrate high standards, how will this candidate compare with others? Note that the question is not: "What is the best kind of postgraduate education?" or "How are you going to use your PGEA sessions?" It deliberately tests how the candidate might react to a difficult situation and improve it.

- Can she salvage the loss and turn it to good account?

- Does she have suggestions for discovering why it happened in the first place?

- How might she prevent it happening again?

- Can she work with others in developing systems that give early warning of problems like this one?

These are not easy questions, particularly for a doctor who is finishing training and has not yet had the benefit of time and experience.

A good answer would include ideas such as a practice meeting to discuss the cause and consequences of the complaint; a description of how a critical event audit might be conducted; involvement of the relevant members of the staff to hear their views and suggestions; proposals for reviewing the communication systems within the practice and auditing the implementation of the new system; examining her own position to ensure that she is competent to deal with a similar emergency; and evidence of her ability to obtain the necessary information from books, journals or other sources to increase her competence.

By now the half-hour will have elapsed, the bell or gong will sound again, and to the candidate's undoubted relief the examination is at an end. The candidates leave the room to do whatever it is that will relieve the tension of the moment. The examiners consider their marks and come to a final judgement. In the case described here it would seem that although the quality of the answers was generally good and excellent in some places, in others they lacked confidence or revealed gaps in the knowledge base. There were no serious lapses, however, and there was consistent evidence of ability in all areas tested. It was perhaps not consistent enough to justify an 'Excellent' grade, but all in all thoroughly justified the acceptance of her application to be a Member of the Royal College of General Practitioners.

References

Forrest Report (1986) *Breast Cancer Screening. Report to the Health Ministers of England, Wales, Scotland and Northern Ireland.* London, HMSO.

Underwood MJ and Bailey JS (1993) Coronary bypass surgery should not be offered to smokers. *British Medical Journal* **306**, 1047–50.

Wilson JMG (1965) Some principles of early diagnosis and detection. In *Surveillance and Early Diagnosis in General Practice.* Proceedings of Colloquium held at Magdalen College, Oxford. Ed. Teeling-Smith G. London, Office of Health Economics. pp 5–10.

14 After the MRCGP Examination

The new Member of the Royal College of General Practitioners can justifiably be pleased with success in the examination, for it is not easily achieved. The fact that nearly two thousand candidates choose to sit the examination each year testifies to its acceptability, for doing so is entirely voluntary though no doubt also advantageous. That one quarter of those that take it each time are not successful shows that it is no easy attainment.

That success may be seen, rightly, as the culmination of ten or more years of studious application to a complex and difficult subject, which demands many varied qualities in its practitioners. At the same time passing the examination is only the beginning, for such is the pace of change in the profession today that without further application the knowledge and skills learned with so much hard work will soon be outmoded and the attitudes with which they were applied will become inappropriate. How then should the new member view the future, and how should the education so laudably undertaken before continue amongst the many other professional and personal demands upon the time and energy of a general practitioner?

In passing the examination the new member of the College has not only demonstrated achievement of the level of competence required for independent practice, but has joined a professional organization dedicated to promoting and maintaining high standards in general practice. It is therefore of the greatest importance that those who have qualified for membership should maintain it by remaining subscribing members. Regrettably there is a tendency to allow subscriptions to lapse when the examination is over, for to some the College may appear not to have immediate or local advantages, and this is understandable given the pressures, often very large, on the financial, personal and professional resources of a new general practitioner. It is, however, a short-sighted view for not only does the College need its members and their subscriptions but the profession of general practice needs a College which can debate the issues of the day with enlightened authority, can proclaim the quality which it should strive to achieve, and can support its members with the necessary research, education and services. These were the objectives which our predecessors in the nineteenth century dreamed of, and which our founders worked so hard to achieve. We must follow their lead and, building on the foundations they have laid, seek that excellence to which a great profession should aspire.

The new member may well ask where continuing education should begin, and in one way that is difficult to answer, for general practice is so wide a discipline. An open mind which is receptive to new ideas and willing to reconsider old ones is essential, and an attitude which learns from experience informed by research will ensure progress. The member may also ask how the College can help, and what other paths can be followed to further the aims of continuing education. To answer these questions it may help to glance over our shoulders at the past, and then look to the foreseeable future, and possibly beyond.

Achievements so far

It is but one professional lifetime, just over forty years, since the College was founded. From the point of view of the contemporary practitioner it is hard to imagine the despondency with which the profession viewed its future at that time, and to realize the great progress which has been made since then.

Looking back over the forty years since then it is evident that the Royal College of General Practitioners has been a major force in the development of general practice, not only in Britain but throughout the world. It is this dedication by its members and the leading individuals within the membership which has established general practice as both a practical and an academic discipline in its own right within the medical profession.

131

In a review article to celebrate the first forty years of the College's history Pereira Gray (1992a) discusses the progress made in the light of the founding Steering Committee's aims. High on the list were the provision of a headquarters and the giving of a lead to general practice, and to plan and follow an agreed policy on matters of importance. Next came education for general practice, which not only promoted the idea, then novel if not revolutionary, of introducing general practice as a subject in the undergraduate curriculum but also initiated postgraduate training of qualified doctors before entering practice and their continuing education throughout their careers. Also among their aims were the enhancement of the esteem with which general practitioners were held by students, specialists and the public; the improvement of the quality and skill of practice by the setting of high standards in parallel with the other Royal Colleges; and the introduction of a diploma to demonstrate the competence of general practitioners in the 'breadth' of the subjects necessary for practice.

The College has achieved all these aims and more. Not only does it have its headquarters at Princes Gate, but it has a faculty structure which makes participation in locally-based College activities a practical possibility for all members. The expansion in education has been huge, with the foundation of departments of general practice in universities and medical schools and the appointment of regional advisers to oversee the postgraduate programmes. Above all the College has led the way in developing the vocational training programme. These initiatives have enabled the expansion of research, the creation of a body of literature relevant to the needs of general practitioners, and the recognition of general practice as a discipline in its own right; indeed they have met the exact objectives which Dr James Cole and Dr George Ross set out so eloquently in 1844. In his historical review Pereira Gray (1992a) describes these achievements as "a liberating movement on a grand scale". Furthermore the College's motto, *Cum Scientia Caritas,* science with compassion, though chosen at a time when Latin was rather more significant in medical education than it is today, expresses the twin objectives of all general practitioners. The General Practice Steering Committee (1953) described its idea of a diploma examination as "an emblem of quality worth striving for". How does the new member, wearing that emblem and wishing to be compassionate and scientific, maintain and develop the skills and the wisdom so necessary for the task that lies ahead, evolving and changing as the years go by?

Opportunities for learning in practice

The introduction of the postgraduate education allowance in 1990 gave a stimulus to educational activity that produced many new ideas, but opportunity is not synonymous with achievement. The network of postgraduate tutors, now funded by the Department of Health and recognized as essential to the provision of continuing education for general practitioners on a local basis, originated in the decision to appoint local 'College tutors' in the 1970s. Mere attendance at a postgraduate session, though measurable, does not guarantee learning, the measurement or demonstration of which is more difficult. How then, can a general practitioner find and choose the best methods for his or her continuing education? Undoubtedly the answer to that is that learning must be largely self-directed, varied according to individual needs, and resourced by both the individual and the collective resources of practices and the profession.

A model for developing a self-directed approach is described by Stanley and colleagues (1993a). It consists of three major sources of learning, which could and should become an everyday part of general practice. Until the final test of preparation, that is until taking the MRCGP at the end of training, the student or junior doctor has often been the object of didactic teaching, and the change to self-directed learning at a time of much other change in status and activity must be a conscious and deliberate one. The three sources of learning which Stanley and his colleagues describe are: reading, to provide the firm knowledge base; experience, to allow the knowledge acquired to be put in context and used; and reflection, to enable the knowledge and experience to be developed to meet individual circumstance.

Central to all is the concept of audit, not as a contractual requirement directed from outside but as a means of capturing experience and processing it in order to learn from it. They emphasize that the place of work is the natural setting for learning

(Stanley et al., 1993b). The individual doctor in directing learning must select, organize and interpret the experience gained in practice to meet individual needs. This may be done through the opportunities provided by structured postgraduate activities such as lectures or courses, distance learning packages and by more or less informal peer group meetings. It may also be achieved by the stimulus of teaching others, by research and writing, or through small group activities. Having directed learning where it was required, the doctor will wish to know whether the learning is being applied well, and thus audit again plays its part in the process of learning. Such audit may be a personal activity or shared with others; in either case it must be meaningful for the individual learner and free from external demands or pressures.

It might be thought that, arriving at partnership at the age of thirty, a general practitioner has little in the way of career progress for another thirty years. Indeed so it used to be, and still can be unless the effort is made to look for challenges and opportunities. Two important features of adult learning are that it should be based on the personal experiences and needs of the learners, and should be generated from their everyday work or life activities. How then can a general practitioner, under pressure from the demands of the practice, create such challenges and opportunities?

An educational career structure is described by Pietroni (1992), the first stages of which are already in place, and the later stages are all available now. The early stages are the undergraduate training, preregistration work and vocational training schemes, leading to the MRCGP examination, and when they are implemented the summative assessment procedures. Thereafter there are opportunities to study for an MSc or doctorate in relevant subjects, and through continuing education to Fellowship of the Royal College of General Practitioners. But because these opportunities may require that a curriculum be followed they may be too prescriptive to meet the needs of individuals. Therefore the concept of portfolio-based learning is described (RCGP, 1993a). This would involve the collection of evidence of learning by an individual, based on his or her needs and interests and consisting of case records, videorecordings, audit and research work and evidence of personal learning. This evidence would then be considered with a mentor or supervisor to enhance the learning

134

doctor' and 'The partnership' have 52 and 17 criteria respectively, but 'The profession' has no essential criteria being divided into four areas of activity which may be considered. An outline of the areas assessed under each heading are shown in Table 14.1, and full details may be obtained on application to the College.

Table 14.1 The areas considered in Fellowship by Assessment

- **The doctor**
  Entry requirements
  Accessibility
  Clinical services
  The consultation
  Other communication skills
  Performance review
  Personal qualities
  Postgraduate education

- **The partnership**
  The practice
  Staff
  Library
  Practice information

- **The profession**
  Medical activities
  Writing
  Services to society
  Services to the College

It is important to realize that although the headings remain consistent, standards are never static and therefore the criteria themselves are reviewed annually by the Council in the light of advancing research and clinical practice.

At first sight it may seem as though the process is somewhat prescriptive in that it defines areas for attention. It does not, however, direct how those areas should be developed. For instance, although Criterion A48 requires that the candidate should present for assessment 10 of his or her own written plans or protocols for the management of diseases, and does indicate how such a plan should be presented, it does not prescribe what the methods of management should be. The candidate must obtain the necessary information from the literature and relate that to the particular needs of the practice. Criterion A50 requires the 'commitment to case audit' of six types of emergency but does not define how the candidate should deal with the cases; it is for the candidate to demonstrate that a proper audit has been done in the way which is most suitable to circumstances. A selection of videotaped consultations must be assessed, and the process of assessment is defined to ensure comparability between assessors. The candidate is an active participant in the process, and analyses the performance as part of the preparation, thereby contributing to the learning process.

Preparation for the assessment thus sets goals to achieve, and because the achievements are to be tested, acts as both guide and stimulus to encourage the candidate to direct his or her own learning. As a long-term target for the new member of the College the prospect of working towards Fellowship by Assessment holds many advantages, not least by offering a structure for the developments that must be made and a support system for the difficulties that may be encountered in making them.

There can be no doubt that the educational challenge of reaching the standard required for Fellowship by Assessment is a demanding one which will amply reward those who are eager to continue their learning.

New Fellows by Assessment

Although at the time of writing (autumn 1993) only 30 members have so far passed this new quality assurance programme the important fact is that the numbers have doubled in the last year and 15 new Fellows by Assessment were presented to the Annual General Meeting of the College in November 1993. This implies that this new assurance programme is taking off and it already far exceeds the only other effective rival, BS5750, which is very much more expensive, less directly relevant to general practice and requires substantial annual expenses thereafter. It is therefore likely that not only membership but Fellowship of the College obtained in this way will both become increasingly important in the years ahead.

Benefit for general practice

Apart from these practical opportunities for individual membership of the College, there are some important consequences of this new system which will benefit general practice as a whole. By defining the gold standard of general practice, the College has given a target for all general practitioners and a new logic in assessing the effectiveness of continuing medical education for general practitioners. By building up a steadily increasing number of general practitioners of whom everyone can be proud, the College has started to spread the model of good general practice around the British Isles and will in passing increasingly benefit from the data which this well organized system of care will provide.

Re-accreditation

The idea that general practitioners are willing to learn through the medium of peer review, and to subject themselves to scrutiny by others, reflects the possibility now being openly discussed of some form of periodic re-accreditation or re-certification. If summative assessment at the end of vocational training becomes a reality, as the Joint Committee on Postgraduate Training for General Practice proposes (JCPTGP, 1993), this will provide the basic accreditation. It has been suggested that if an agreement on standards and how to demonstrate their attainment can be achieved, the knowledge that they will be tested periodically will be a powerful incentive for general practitioners to ensure that their own continuing education is effective and thorough (Silver, 1989). Such an incentive would no doubt be effective, but the difficulty lies in reaching agreement, not only on the appropriate standards but on the methods of assessment. Many practices willingly undergo assessment to become training practices, and externally imposed targets for cervical cytology and immunization procedures have been effective, which show that such incentives can work. However, acceptance of such scrutiny is voluntary and the introduction of compulsory procedures which might threaten to disrupt a doctor's livelihood would be an entirely different matter.

The aims of accreditation have been described by Pereira Gray (1992b) as "to ensure that the places in which practice and learning take place are fully satisfactory and appropriate for the purpose and that the doctor, when accredited, is fully competent for the tasks which he or she may have to undertake". He takes the view that accreditation will undoubtedly be introduced at some time in the future, not only for individual doctors but also for the settings in which they work. How this will be done is yet to be debated. Formidable problems remain to be resolved. For instance, how can assessment procedures be developed which are demonstrably valid, reliable, feasible and acceptable? How can they be made to reflect the events and challenges of general practice, and to sample the whole range of the practitioner's activities? Therein lies the difficulty, for we have yet to define what constitutes the essence of general practice, let alone set standards throughout its range by which judgements can be made on the adequacy of its practitioners (Stanley I, personal communication).

The College is making a leading contribution to the debate about accreditation. It takes the view that the essence of such a procedure is not only to provide evidence of adequate standards within the profession but to provide a focus and support for the continuing education necessary to ensure those standards (Toby J, personal communication).

It is not the purpose of this chapter to discuss the detail of accreditation and re-accreditation, but to mention the idea that the subject is now open for debate. Candidates now taking the MRCGP examination are the College's members of the future. Not only must they plan their continuing education bearing in mind the probability that in the not-too-distant future they will face the challenge of re-accreditation; they would do well to remain active members of the College so that they may contribute to the debate which will surround its introduction, and influence the form which it will take. The College needs its membership to be broadly based, for only then can it truly represent the profession in promoting ways to meet its continuing educational needs.

References

General Practice Steering Committee (1953) A college of general practitioners. *Practitioner* **170**. Suppl.

Gray DJ Pereira (1992a) History of the Royal College of General Practitioners. *British Journal of General Practice* **42**, 29–35.

Gray DJ Pereira (1992b) Accreditation in general practice. *Quality in Health Care* **1**, 61–4.

Irvine D (1983) Quality of care in general practice: our outstanding problem. *Journal of the Royal College of General Practitioners* **33**, 521–3.

Joint Committee on Postgraduate Training for General Practice (1993) Report of the Summative Assessment Working Party. London, JCPTGP. Unpublished.

Pietroni R (1992) New strategies for higher professional education. *British Journal of General Practice* **42**, 294–6.

Royal College of General Practitioners (1990) *Fellowship by Assessment. Occasional Paper 50*. London, RCGP.

Royal College of General Practitioners (1992) Guide and criteria for Fellowship by Assessment of the Royal College of General Practitioners. 4th version. London, RCGP.

Royal College of General Practitioners (1993a) *Portfolio-based Learning in General Practice. Occasional Paper 63*. London, RCGP.

Royal College of General Practitioners (1993b) Council Report. *Connection*. August, p. 1.

Royal College of General Practitioners (1993c) Now—what shall we do? The next three years. Council report, 10 July.

Silver T (1989) Certification and re-certification—a time and a place for action. *Journal of the Royal Society of Medicine* **82**, 251–2.

Stanley I, Al-Shehri A and Thomas P (1993a) Continuing education for general practice. 1. Experience, competence and the media of self-directed learning for general practitioners. *British Journal of General Practice* **43**, 210–4.

Stanley I, Al-Shehri A and Thomas P (1993b) Continuing education for general practice. 2. Systematic learning from experience. *British Journal of General Practice* **43**, 249–53.

15 Possible Future Developments

The MRCGP examination is always under review to ensure that it meets the needs both of the College and the candidates. As a result of continuous research and observation, as well as the growing experience and expertise of the examiners, it is constantly developing, mostly by evolution rather than revolution. From time to time, however, the pace of change quickens, and while no revolution seems probable at present, there are likely to be considerable alterations in the next few years. An outline of the form which these might take is given in this chapter, which represents the author's personal understanding of them and should not be construed as the policy of the College, the Examination Board or the Panel of Examiners.

An examination as comprehensive as the MRCGP has a dual role: the major one of testing the competence of its candidates and a secondary and consequential one of setting an agenda for learning. That is not to say that the examination dogmatically sets out to prescribe what should be learned, but it is inevitable that if something is to be tested it will to a greater or lesser extent be rehearsed. Two examples will suffice to show how the MRCGP examination has influenced how and what its candidates learn: the decision to introduce pre-certification in cardiovascular resuscitation has ensured that thousands of candidates have learned this technique, have been tested and have shown an acceptable degree of proficiency; and the emphasis in the CRQ and the orals on candidates' knowledge of current literature because of its importance in rational decision-making appears to have greatly increased their activity in this respect, though whether these are cause and effect has not been demonstrated (Wakeford and Southgate, 1992). The Examination Board and the nuclear groups of examiners who originate the new ideas are well aware of the responsibility they have for ensuring that any new developments will not only enhance the examination's reliability and validity but will do nothing to diminish its acceptability or endanger its reputation.

At present the orals cover the whole range of competences, from problem-solving and management to personal and professional growth. To some extent the areas that deal mostly with clinical matters, such as problem-solving, prevention and management, are also examined in the papers. This partly duplicates the testing of these areas, in which it is largely factual knowledge being examined, at the expense of the more attitudinal aspects such as communication skills, professional values and personal and professional growth. There is some merit in the suggestion that less time should be spent on the former to allow more attention to be paid to the latter which, being concerned with individual attitudes and beliefs, are best examined in face-to-face discussion. No decision about this has been made, but it is mentioned here as an example of the way in which examination methods are always under review to ensure that they remain relevant and effective.

One area in which the MRCGP examination is open to criticism is that it has no direct way of testing what the candidates actually do in practice. It has no clinical component, so that all judgements are about the competence of candidates (what they are capable of doing) rather than about their performance (what they do in practice) (Cox and Mulholland, 1993a). So should there be a system for directly assessing clinical activity, and if so what form should it take? To do this would necessitate some examination of candidates' activity in consultations, including physical and psychological examination, and to be totally comprehensive it would also need to test practical and technical skills of various kinds. To examine two thousand candidates a year in this way with a high degree of consistency and reliability would be a formidable task. Nevertheless the problem has been addressed and three possible methods of doing so have been explored.

Objective structured clinical examination

The objective structured clinical examination (OSCE) has been used in the formative assessment of trainees in the West Cumbria

143

Vocational Training Scheme (Walker and Walker, 1987) and has been used as a form of summative assessment in the membership examination of the Irish College of General Practitioners since 1987. This provides for a number of 'stations', that is to say clinical problems or other test situations, which are set out in the examination hall and which the candidates visit in turn. The stations may involve people role-playing patients, or materials such as x-ray plates, case notes, photographs or ECG recordings. At each station an examiner observes the candidate and awards marks according to a previously agreed schedule.

In the method used by the Irish College of General Practitioners there are 10 stations in the OSCE, which contributes 25% of the total marks available, with 25% being contributed by the orals and 50% by the papers. The Irish College has only 60 candidates at each examination, however, and reliability, though improving with experience, is not as good as the College would wish. Efforts are continuing to improve the method, probably adding more stations and additional topics (Coffey B, personal communication).

The advantages of the OSCE are considerable in that it is objective, as its name implies, because the candidate is directly observed at work on the task without the intrusive influence of an examiner. The marking schedules can be applied consistently between candidates, unlike the orals which are highly individual and vary according to both examiner and candidate. The range of suitable subjects is considerable and can include history-taking and psychological problems using appropriately trained personnel. Walker and Walker (1987) showed that it can be very useful as a method of formative assessment during training, where feedback can be given to the trainees who can take steps to improve where necessary. In the MRCGP, however, it would pose considerable logistical problems. One thousand candidates at each diet of the examination would need huge numbers of role-players and examiners, much space and time, and would present problems of consistency and reliability. It would probably add considerably to the cost of the examination, and that is not likely to find favour with candidates. No plans are being actively considered to introduce OSCE at present whatever its merits in other situations may be.

Simulated surgeries

Another approach is the examination of candidates by direct observation of 'simulated surgeries'. This system allows candidates to remain in the same place, namely a consulting room, real or simulated, while a series of role-playing patients is presented to them (Bingham, 1991). It is thus a development of the OSCE with the various 'stations' being brought to the candidate in a consulting room rather then being set out in an examination hall. It builds on the strengths of the OSCE by using its features in a more realistic setting.

The process of the consultation is assessed by one or more observers, either by direct vision or through one way mirrors or closed circuit television. In an examination this could provide the opportunity to assess skills necessary for history-taking, problem identification and communication in a realistic way, using a prepared marking schedule to establish consistency of assessment. The presence of an observer, whether in the room or through television, introduces an element absent from the real consultation, but so does the whole process of assessment.

Similarly problems may arise with the closed circuit television or videorecording in quality of reproduction or technical failure, which makes this unsuitable for examination purposes. As the process is simulated it would not be possible to assess some practical skills of examination where positive physical signs would be expected, nor certain manual skills. The same problems of logistics and resources apply to simulated surgeries as to OSCEs. Despite these difficulties a working party of the Examination Board has considered the possibility of using simulated surgeries as a method of assessing clinical skills and how it might contribute to the examination. No decision to introduce the method has yet been made, but it is certainly seen as a promising area.

Videorecording

The use of videorecording is now widespread as a means of studying consultations in vocational training schemes and is extensively used as a teaching tool in other disciplines in medicine and elsewhere. It has the ability to capture real-life situations with little or no apparent intrusion. It would therefore seem to lend itself to the recording of candidates' actual work, which could be submitted to the examiners for assessment as a part of the MRCGP examination. It would have the merits of being the 'real thing', of revealing the actual performance of the candidate, thereby complementing the assessment of competence inferred from other parts of the examination, and of including aspects such as some physical signs and manual skills less easily observed by other methods. It is not without its difficulties, however, but its potential is such that much work has been done to develop a practical method of using it in the examination.

The method favoured at present is that candidates would be required to make videotapes of a series of consultations. They would then analyse the consultations in the 'work-book' provided, which invites critical observations about them, such as how well the candidate had perceived the patients' reasons for attendance and had agreed management plans; what kind of non-verbal communication was used and how it was interpreted and responded to; or how well a range of possible diagnoses and investigations had been considered. The candidate's own observations would then be considered in relation to the performance observed by the examiner on playing the videotapes.

A method of marking has been devised consisting of certain 'performance criteria', that is to say elements which were considered to be necessary for a performance to be judged as adequate. Some of these criteria will be deemed 'desirable', indicating that it is expected that most candidates would achieve most of them, taking into account the level of ability of candidates at the time, and if they were consistently achieved the candidate would be assessed as competent. Failure to achieve each and every criterion would not be critical, but frequent failures would clearly indicate poor performance. Some criteria will be 'exceptional', that is they would be achieved by very able candidates who might be exceptional trainees or more experienced doctors such as principals of some years' standing. At the other end of the scale would be those criteria which were deemed 'mandatory', in the sense that if the candidate failed to achieve them it might indicate lack of competence or even potentially dangerous practice (Foulkes and Tate, 1993).

146

The same logistical and financial constraints apply to the videotaped consultation method of assessing performance as to the other methods, but to a lesser degree. Much of the cost would be borne within the training practices for those candidates still in training, and for others it would be moderate. Examiner time is an important factor, for it would undoubtedly require a much bigger commitment and more examiners might be needed.

More difficult to resolve are the issues of confidentiality and of whether the knowledge that an assessment of the doctor's performance is taking place would alter the consultation process. The question of confidentiality has been addressed by the Oral Development Group, who are working out procedure, and a report to Council has been accepted in which stringent rules are laid down to protect confidentiality of patients and the interests of doctors submitting examples of their work (RCGP, 1993).

Considerable doubt has been expressed about using this method in summative assessment, and by implication in the MRCGP examination (Baird and Gillies, 1993). They quote the experience of the West of Scotland Postgraduate Education Committee which introduced the method as part of summative assessment and found considerable opposition from trainers and trainees on the grounds of interference with the consultations being assessed and the threat to career prospects from those deemed to be lacking in certain attributes. Similarly a considerable proportion of patients who were asked about their attitude to such recordings expressed doubts about its desirability and its effects on their consultations (Bain and Mackay, 1993). On the other hand Cox and Mulholland (1993a,b) have shown it to be a satisfactory method in formative assessment and, given safeguards adequate to ensure validity, which means having the proper relationship between the number of consultations examined and the number of markers, it could be used in summative assessment.

Because it is judged to be the most promising way of assessing performance, examination using videotaped consultations was planned on a trial basis for the autumn 1993 diet. Volunteer candidates were used and the results did not contribute to the marking process for the examination as a whole. Candidates willing to do this deserve the same credit as do the five who took the first examination in 1965, which, being the first such test of competence in a long established discipline, must have seemed just as threatening.

MRCGP and summative assessment

Perhaps the most important unanswered question about the future of the MRCGP examination is how it will fit into the pattern of summative assessment of training for general practice. It has been taken entirely voluntarily by a substantial majority of doctors concluding their training, though perhaps as much in the hope that membership of the College will help them in their career as from pure altruism. Since it became necessary to have a certificate of satisfactory completion of training very few trainees have failed to obtain such a certificate, which is awarded without any formal assessment and on the basis of the opinions of those who have contributed to the training, which may not be entirely objective. On the other hand, about 25% of those who choose to take the MRCGP examination do not pass it. This indicates a discrepancy of some size between the level of competence demanded by the training authorities and by the Royal College of General Practitioners. Is one too easily satisfied or does the other expect too much? Are they even measuring the same thing?

Four elements

Summative assessment will consist of four elements:

- Tests of factual knowledge and problem-solving

- Evaluation of clinical and consulting skills

- Submission of practical work

- An overall assessment by trainers (JCPTGP, 1993).

The first of these elements is included in the MRCGP examination and will probably be assessed by MCQ and MEQ. The MRCGP also evaluates clinical and consulting skills as far as possible but how this will be done in summative assessment is not yet certain. The possible methods are by examination of videotaped consultations or by simulated surgeries, but a decision has still to be made. The third and fourth elements are not part of the MRCGP and are unlikely to be so. The practical work will consist of an audit project and some other work as yet undefined. Assessment by trainers is well established and familiar, but may be broadened and extended to include some form of log book which has to be completed from time to time throughout training. It is also envisaged that there will be some system by which assessment can be completed in a series of modules rather than in one final summative examination (Allen J, personal communication).

It was originally intended that summative assessment should be administered on a regional basis. However, at the time of writing the amalgamation of the regions has just been announced and it is unclear how educational arrangements will be made in future.

Thus the objectives of the two systems of assessment, while parallel in the sense of testing similar qualities in the same people, are in another sense quite separate. The summative assessment proposals are to ensure minimum standards of competence at the end of training, and in effect to monitor the quality of the training process by testing its product. The MRCGP examination, however, retains its original purpose of being the normal route of entry to the Royal College of General Practitioners, and as such demonstrates the candidates' ability to reach not only the minimum standard but that degree of competence which a learned profession and a discriminating public reasonably demand. It is the foundation for a career in general practice which in future will include continuing education as an increasingly important activity. At the time of writing it is not clear how far the JCPTGP and RCGP policies will intertwine. This is under active discussion. Recently successful candidates in the examination for Membership of the Royal College of General Practitioners should be proud of their achievement. They will also do well to reflect that it is not only the culmination of many years of hard work in preparation for their careers but is also a new beginning in a life-long process of learning by study and experience. It is a long and sometimes arduous road, but to follow it is a challenge to which all doctors who take pride in their professional stature should aspire.

References

Bain J and Mackay NOD (1993) Videotaping general practice consultations. Letter. *British Medical Journal* **307**, 504–5.

Baird AG and Gillies JCM (1993) Assessing GPs' performance; Videotape assessment is threatening. Letter. *British Medical Journal* **307**, 60.

Bingham L (1991) Simulated surgeries as a method of assessment. *Horizons*, November, 438–50.

Cox J and Mulholland H (1993a) An instrument for assessment of videotapes of general practitioners' performance. *British Medical Journal* **306**, 1043–6.

Cox J and Mulholland H (1993b) Assessing GPs' performance. Letter. *British Medical Journal* **307**, 60.

Foulkes J and Tate P (1993) Memorandum to the Panel of Examiners, RCGP. Unpublished.

Joint Committee on Postgraduate Training for General Practice (1993) Report of the Summative Assessment Working Party. London, JCPTGP. Unpublished.

Royal College of General Practitioners (1993) *Statement on the Use of Video-Recording of General Practice Consultations for Teaching, Learning and Assessment: The Importance of Ethical Considerations.* Ed. Southgate L. London, RCGP.

Wakeford R and Southgate L (1992) Postgraduate medical education: modifying trainees' approaches by changing the examination. *Teaching and Learning in Medicine* **4**, 210–13.

Walker R and Walker B (1987) Use of the objective structured clinical examination for assessment of vocational trainees for general practitioners. *Journal of the Royal College of General Practitioners* **37**, 123–4.

APPENDIX 1

The Royal College of General Practitioners
14 Princes Gate, London, SW7 1PU
071-581 3232

APPLICATION FORM FOR MEMBERSHIP
(Updated 1993)

Information will be treated as strictly confidential.

PERSONAL DETAILS

1. TITLE ⌊_____⌋

2. INITIALS ⌊_____⌋

3. FORENAME ⌊_____⌋

4. SURNAME ⌊_____⌋

5. SEX ⌊⌋   6. DATE OF BIRTH ⌊___/___/___⌋

7. MAILING ADDRESS

⌊_____⌋

⌊_____⌋

⌊_____⌋

⌊_____⌋

POST CODE ⌊_____⌋

COUNTRY ⌊_____⌋

8. GMC NUMBER ⌊_____⌋

9. DATE OF FULL REGISTRATION ⌊___/___/___⌋
(Please attach a photocopy of your current certificate of Registration)

10. CONTACT TELEPHONE NUMBERS

Daytime ⌊_____⌋ Home ⌊_____⌋

Completed application forms should be returned to the Examination Department at the address given above by   . Please make sure that you have enclosed your examination application fee and certificates attesting competence in basic cardio-pulmonary resuscitation and child health surveillance.

151

11. Vocational Training for General Practice

    (a) Have you undergone or are you currently undergoing vocational training?   YES/NO

    (b) If yes, please give dates of commencement and completion

    |_____| |_____|

    (c) If you have completed vocational training what is your current post?

    ....

    (d) Are you currently serving in one of the armed services? YES/NO

12. Have you sat the MRCGP Examination before?   YES/NO

13. Please indicate when and where you wish to sit the written papers

    date ....   venue..

14. Please indicate where you wish to attend for oral examination ....

    Please indicate if you will have difficulty in attending for oral examination on any particular day or if you wish to attend on a specific day ....

    ....

15. Country of birth: ....

16. Date of qualification:...

17. Medical school ....

18. Qualifying degree or diploma: ....

19. Postgraduate diplomas: ....

20. Are you at present an associate of the College?   YES/NO

FOR OFFICE USE	
DVT	
T	
RT	
APPS	
WPC	
OC	
OD	
OT	

21. **HOSPITAL EXPERIENCE**

   (i) Pre-Registration posts:

Hospital	Specialty	Consultant	Date Commenced	Date Completed

FOR OFFICE USE

   (ii) After Registration with the General Medical Council

Hospital	Specialty	Status of Post	Consultant	Date Commenced	Date Completed

22. **GENERAL PRACTICE EXPERIENCE**

   (i) Experience as a Trainee General Practitioner:

Name and Address of Trainer	Date Commenced	Date Completed

   (ii) Other General practice experience:

Address of Practice	Status of Post	Date Commenced	Date Completed

23. **OTHER POST-REGISTRATION EXPERIENCE**

....

....

24. CANDIDATE'S STATEMENT

I hereby apply to sit the examination for membership of The Royal College of General Practitioners. If accepted for membership I undertake to continue approved postgraduate study while I remain in active general practice, and to uphold and promote the aims of the College to the best of my ability.

Date .... Signature of applicant ....

25. POSTGRADUATE EDUCATION FOR GENERAL PRACTICE

Have you experience as a Trainee Practitioner? YES/NO

If YES, please specify:

(1) As part of a three year Pre-planned programme within a scheme and including day/half-day release

(2) As part of an independent (self-constructed) three year programme including day/half-day release

(3) As part of any period of postgraduate experience but not including day release

Please complete details of your programme as appropriate:-

Region/Armed service ....

Scheme (Postgraduate Centre) .... Date of Completion ....

Day/half-day release course location .... Number of half-day sessions ....

26. Have you attended any specific course of preparation for the MRCGP examination? YES/NO

If YES, please specify:

Location ....

Number of half-day sessions ....

27. ENDORSEMENT OF APPLICATION

Candidates entering the examination within one year of completing vocational training (whether Pre-planned or Independent) are required to have their application form endorsed by their Postgraduate Dean, Regional Adviser, Associate Adviser in General Practice or Course Organiser.

I certify that this candidate has completed/or will complete on .... a period of vocational training for general practice as outlined above.

Signature: ....

Name and Designation: ....

ROYAL COLLEGE OF GENERAL PRACTITIONERS

EXAMINATION FOR MEMBERSHIP

CARDIO-PULMONARY RESUSCITATION (CPR) - NOTES FOR CANDIDATES AND TESTERS

All candidates applying to sit the MRCGP examination must provide evidence of competence in basic cardio-pulmonary resuscitation (CPR).

Certification

The certificate printed overleaf, which is based on the guidelines for basic life support issued by the Basic Life Support Working Party of the European Resuscitation Council in November 1992, when completed, will certify vvsatisfactory performance in basic cardio-pulmonary resuscitation for the purposes of the examination. *No other form of certification will be acceptable.* The certificate will remain valid for three years. Candidates resitting the examination within this period are not required to undertake a further test.

The ideal performance of each activity and acceptable levels of variation are itemised on the certificate. The candidate must be able to achieve a pass in each activity but those who fail may be re-tested after instruction.

Candidates who do not live in the United Kingdom or the Republic of Ireland and perceive difficulty in completing the test by the closing date for applications are asked to contact the Examination Administrator for advice. **The Certificate issued must accompany the application form for Membership unless agreed otherwise.** If you are physically challenged and incapable of carrying out cardio-pulmonary resuscitation, please ask the tester to certify that you are competent in instructing a physically able person to perform CPR to the requisite level. A note should be made on the form if certification has been achieved in this way.

Testing

Many candidates will have access to hospital specialists in accident and emergency departments and anaesthetic departments. A certificate signed by a hospital consultant in the departments of accident and emergency and anaesthetics or by others with specific skills will be accepted. These could include general practitioners or doctors in HM Forces with a special interest and training officers in the Ambulance Service, Red Cross or St John Ambulance. The Examination Board reserves the right to enquire into the credentials of those issuing certificates as part of its policy of maintaining high standards in its assessment procedures. It welcomes enquiries from those who might be uncertain of their position in regard to the certification of a candidate. Alternatively the ambulance training/testing centres listed on the attached sheet are likely to offer local training and certification.

Any expenses incurred, including fees, are the responsibility of the candidate. We understand that there may be some variation in the charges levied for training and testing between centres because of local charging policies.

The College is grateful to those assessors who undertake testing on its behalf.

December 1993 (test certificate overleaf)

THE ROYAL COLLEGE OF GENERAL PRACTITIONERS
EXAMINATION FOR MEMBERSHIP

CARDIO-PULMONARY RESUSCITATION PERFORMANCE TEST
Revised March 1993
Candidates must obtain a pass in each activity

Candidate's Name _____   Date _____

Activity	Ideal Performance	Acceptable Variation	Pass	Fail
Check for personal safety before treating the casualty 1 Determine unresponsiveness	Shake by shoulders- ask loudly " are you alright?"	None		
2 Call for help	Call for help immediately	None		
3 Open airway and check mouth	Head tilt and chin lift	None		
4 Determine whether casualty is breathing or not	Look, listen and feel for breathing for 5 seconds	None		
5 Determine whether a pulse is present or not	Palpate carotid artery for 5 seconds	None		
6 Activate 999 system	---------	None		
7 Initial Ventilations	2 slow ventilations Vol per ventilations 0.8 - 1.2 litres Inspiratory time per ventilation 2 seconds	1 - 3 slow ventilations		
8 Cycles of chest compressions and ventilations	15 chest compressions to a depth of 4 - 5 cms over the lower part of the sternum avoiding pressure on the abdomen or ribs. at least 70% correct ventilations at least 70% correct compressions Alternate 15 compressions at a rate of 80 per minute with 2 ventilations. Vol per ventilation 0.8 -1.2 litres. Inspiratory time per ventilation of 2 seconds. At least 4 cycles of compressions and ventilations must be performed.	Compression rate 60-100 per minute Average compression : ventilation ratio over assessment period 15:2		
9 Timing of activities	Step 1 to the completion of 4 cycles of compressions/ventilations to be performed within 2 minutes.	Performed within 2 minutes 15 seconds		

Examiner's Signature _____   Result: Pass _____ Fail _____

Professional Status _____

Name _____   *Candidates who fail the test may be re-tested after instruction*

Address _____

ATTACH MANIKIN PERFORMANCE RECORD IF AVAILABLE
THIS CERTIFICATE REMAINS VALID FOR THREE YEARS FROM DATE OF THE TEST

AMBULANCE SERVICE TRAINING/TESTING CENTRES

You are advised to contact the Chief Ambulance Officer or Training Officer at the locations listed below:

LONDON	Bromley Training Centre Crown Lane Bromley	081 464 7608
	Heathrow Training Centre Heathrow Airport Ambulance Centre Building 450 Northern Perimeter Road Hounslow TW6 1JH	081 759 3056
	Ilford Training Centre Aldborough Road South Ilford	081 983 8974
	Fulham Training Centre Fulham Ambulance Station Seagrave Road London SW6 1RX	071 381 4070
Northern	Newcastle upon Tyne Cleveland Carlisle Durham	091 273 1212 0642 823171/855019 0228 39441 x 45 091 386 4488
Yorkshire	Bradford, W Yorkshire Hull York	0274 651410 0482 561191 0904 628085/8
Trent	Rotherham, S Yorkshire Derbyshire Leicestershire Lincolnshire Nottinghamshire	0709 828820 0332 372441 0533 750700 0522 45171 x 27 0602 296151
East Anglia	Cambridge Norwich Ipswich	0223 411444 0603 424255 0473 49333
North-west Thames	Bedford Welwyn Garden City, Herts	0234 270099 0707 327585
North-east Thames	Chelmsford, Essex	0245 443344
South-east Thames	Eastbourne, E Sussex Maidstone, Kent	0323 21433 0622 747010
South-west Thames	Banstead, Surrey Worthing, W Sussex London SE1	0737 353333 0903 691378 071 928 0333
Wessex	Winchester Ringwood Isle of Wight Chippenham Guernsey Jersey	0962 60421 0202 896111 0983 528500 0249 443939 0481 25211 0534 59000 x 2329 - 2333

Oxford

	Wokingham, Berks	0734 771200
	Deanshanger, Milton Keynes	0908 262422
	Oxford	0865 741841

South-western

	Bristol	0272 277046
	Truro, Cornwall	0872 78181
	Exeter	0392 403339
	Gloucester	0452 395050
	Taunton, Somerset	0823 278114

West Midlands

	Dudley	0384 455644
	Worcester	0905 830630
	Shrewsbury	0743 64061
	Stafford	0785 61844
	Leamington Spa, Warwickshire	0926 881331

Merseyside

	Liverpool	051 260 5220
	Chester	0244 362492/362632

North-western

	Manchester	061 236 9456
	Preston	0772 862667

SCOTLAND

	Paisley	041 848 1434
	Ayr	0292 284101
	Motherwell	0698 64201
	Glasgow	041 332 6001
	Edinburgh	031 447 8746
	Aberdeen	0224 681656
	Inverness	0463 235789
	Dundee	0382 816070

WALES

	Mold, Clwyd	0352 700227 x 2123
	Caernarfon, Gwynedd	0286 4811/2 x 126
	Caerleon, Gwent	0633 421521
	Carmarthen, Dyfed	0267 233232
	Brecon, Powys	0874 711661
	Swansea	0792 651501 x 227
	Pontypridd, Mid-Glam	0443 217005
	Cardiff	0222 552011
	Haverfordwest, Dyfed	0437 767801 x 247

NORTHERN IRELAND

	Belfast	0232 246113
	Antrim	08494 67097
	Armagh	0762 335121
	Londonderry	0504 45171

REPUBLIC OF IRELAND

	Dr Gerard Bury	
	Department of General Practice	
	Royal College of Surgeons of Ireland	
	185 Harcourt Street, Dublin 2	0001 784422

candnote.cpr

THE ROYAL COLLEGE OF GENERAL PRACTITIONERS

EXAMINATION FOR MEMBERSHIP

CHILD HEALTH SURVEILLANCE

Notes of guidance for candidates and assessors (March 1992)

All candidates presenting for the Membership examination in 1992 and thereafter are required to provide evidence of their competence in the practical aspects of child health surveillance (CHS) as a pre-entry requirement to the examination. The other elements of the examination will continue to test knowledge, skills and attitudes appropriate to child health surveillance, as before.

Certification

Attached is a form which, when completed by the assessor(s), will certify satisfactory proficiency in child health surveillance. A list of the surveillance tasks which must be demonstrated by the candidate is given on the reverse side of the Certificate. *No other form of certification will be acceptable.* The Certificate will remain valid for three years. Candidates resitting the examination within this period are not required to undertake a further test.

Each age group tested will require a separate signature since it is likely that these examinations will be carried out at different times and possibly in the presence of different assessors. If you do not live in the United Kingdom or the Republic of Ireland and perceive difficulty in completing the test by the closing date for the examination for which you are applying, please contact the Examination Department at the College for advice.

The Certificate must accompany your application form for membership and the examination application fee. Currently there are no exemptions from certification. Those who have been assessed in child health surveillance recently should have little difficulty in obtaining the requisite signatures on the Certificate supplied.

The Examination Department is unable to supply large quantities of certificates for the use of organisers of courses. However, it is permissible for copies of the Certificate to be made, provided that the most up-to-date version available is used for this and the Examination Department will be pleased to advise in this regard.

Assessors

Certification can be carried out by:

(a)   Principals in general practice undertaking child health surveillance on a regular basis and approved to do so by the relevant FHSA or appropriate body

(b)   other doctors, such as consultant community paediatricians and clinical medical officers, currently undertaking child health surveillance under the auspices of a local District Health Authority or appropriate body.

The Examination Board reserves the right to enquire into the credentials of those issuing Certificates as part of its policy of maintaining high standards in its assessment procedures. Enquiries are welcomed from those who might be uncertain of their position in regard to the certification of candidates.

Any expenses incurred are the responsibility of the candidate.

The College is grateful to those assessors who undertake testing on its behalf.

Educational Courses

The Examination Board does not require candidates to have attended specific courses of training in child health surveillance prior to undertaking the test.

ROYAL COLLEGE OF GENERAL PRACTITIONERS
EXAMINATION FOR MEMBERSHIP
CERTIFICATE OF COMPETENCE IN CHILD HEALTH SURVEILLANCE

CANDIDATE'S NAME: ....

1   I have observed this doctor undertaking satisfactorily the examination of a child
    aged 6 - 8 weeks in each of the appropriate surveillance tasks listed overleaf.

Signature:.......................................   Date:..

Name (Block Capitals please):   ....

Address: ....
                                         ....
                                         ....

Professional Status...........................   FHSA/Health Board/
                                         Employing Authority...........................

2   I have observed this doctor undertaking satisfactorily the examination of a child
    aged 6 - 9 months in each of the appropriate surveillance tasks listed overleaf.

Signature:.......................................   Date:..

Name (Block Capitals please):   ....

Address: ....
                                         ....
                                         ....

Professional Status...........................   FHSA/Health Board/
                                         Employing Authority...........................

3   I have observed this doctor undertaking satisfactorily the examination of a child
    aged 36 - 48 months in each of the appropriate surveillance tasks noted overleaf.

Signature:.......................................   Date:..

Name (Block Capitals please):   ....

Address: ....
                                         ....
                                         ....

Professional Status...........................   FHSA/Health Board/
                                         Employing Authority...........................

THIS CERTIFICATE REMAINS VALID FOR THREE YEARS FROM THE DATE OF THE LAST TEST

— 5 —

SECTION F. CLINICAL DIARY

Please list the relevant numbers of patients seen consecutively in each of the following categories:- surgery attendances - 25 cases; home visits - 15 cases; out-of-hours emergencies - 10 cases including 2 night calls whenever possible. These cases will provide examples for examination of your clinical abilities. You may bring brief clinical notes about them to the examination.

No.	Date	Patient's Initials	Age	Sex	Main reason for contact
Surgery Attendances					
1.					
2.					
3.					
4.					
5.					
6.					
7.					
8.					
9.					
10.					
11.					
12.					
13.					
14.					
15.					
16.					
17.					
18.					
19.					
20.					
21.					
22.					
23.					
24.					
25.					

— 6 —

No.	Date	Patient's Initials	Age	Sex	Main reason for contact
Home Visits and repeat visits					
26.					
27.					
28.					
29.					
30.					
31.					
32.					
33.					
34.					
35.					
36.					
37.					
38.					
39.					
40.					

Out-of-hours and emergency calls. Indicate night visits "NV"

If sufficient cases in this category cannot be found please say why this is so.

41.					
42.					
43.					
44.					
45.					
46.					
47.					
48.					
49.					
50.					

Some Questions from Past MCQ Papers

These questions come from a paper set in 1989 and are reproduced from *Occasional Paper 46* (RCGP, 1990) with permission. More recent examples are not available as the questions chosen for each paper come from a stock which may be used repeatedly and is therefore not published. However, they are typical of those in current use. The correct responses are given below each example with comments, and explanations of the way words such as 'recognized' and 'typical' are used.

Example 1

Example 1 shows how the questions are set out in the examination.

The signs and symptoms of parkinsonism:

(a) **characteristically remain unilateral for years**

(b) **are a recognized side effect of amitriptyline therapy**

(c) **are a recognized sequal to encephalitis**

(d) **characteristically include intention tremor**

(e) **are exacerbated by levodopa and carbidopa given in combination.**

Answers and explanatory comments

(a) **False:** It would be very unusual for any of the degenerative processes causing parkinsonism to affect only one hemisphere over several years. If they did this would cast doubt on the original diagnosis; i.e. it would not be a 'characteristic' feature.

(b) **False:** Phenothiazines are 'recognized' to cause parkinsonism but tricyclic antidepressants do not.

(c) **True:** This is the easiest item with 90% getting the correct answer, but with a strong correlation coefficient of 0.33 indicating that poor candidates were getting it wrong or not attempting it.

(d) **False:** Intention tremor is 'characteristic' of cerebellar disease.

(e) **False:** A surprising 17.4% did not realize that levodopa plus carbidopa is Sinemet.

Example 2

Example 2 shows that questions relating to practice organization and other non-clinical areas will occur.

Under the Misuse of Drugs Act 1971:

(a) a pharmacist dispensing a specified drug may be required to supply the name and address of the prescribing doctor

(b) a prescription for a controlled drug must contain the patient's name and address in the doctor's own handwriting

(c) doctors must keep a register of controlled drug transactions in a bound book

(d) a locked car is regarded as a locked receptacle for the safe custody of controlled drugs

(e) any doctor attending a person he suspects is addicted to a controlled drug must inform the appropriate authority within 7 days.

Answers

(a) **True:** Regulation 25 gives a list of authorized persons who can demand from a pharmacist names and addresses of doctors who have prescribed certain drugs. Details must be kept for 2 years.

(b) **True:** Over 10% of candidates in 1989 did not know this.

(c) **True:** The book must be bound, not looseleaf.

(d) **False:** Over 12% did not know this.

(e) **True:** 30% did not know this.

Example 3

Example 3 shows the kind of question which tests Ethical and Legal knowledge.

Mobility Allowance:

(a) is available only to those who hold a current driving licence

(b) can be claimed by a handicapped child of 3 years

(c) can be paid only until the age of 75 years

(d) is available for periods of short-term disability lasting less than 1 year

(e) is automatically available to those on the Blind Register.

Answers

(a) **False:** The allowance is intended to help with transport costs and is for those who are virtually unable to walk.

(b) **False:** It can be claimed for those aged 5–65, but once obtained is paid until the claimant reaches 75, when it stops.

(c) **True:** See (b) above.

(d) **False:** The inability to walk must be likely to last for at least a year.

(e) **False:** Mobility Allowance is for those unable to *walk*.

Other examples

The following extracts from questions illustrate the way in which words are used in the questions:

In presbyacusis (hearing loss due to ageing);

(a) Recruitment is *typically* present

(b) High fibre diets *have been shown* to delay the progress of the condition

(e) Hearing by bone conduction *is unaffected.*

Answers

(a) **True:** It is often observed that the patient cannot hear quiet sounds but may find a louder sound unpleasant because it is 'too loud'; this 'typifies' the condition.

(b) **False:** Even if this is not known for sure a little thought will suggest it is not true, so a 'guess' will be correct.

(e) **False:** A double negative—hearing is *not* unaffected; i.e. it is affected.

In acute epiglottitis:

(a) Haemophilus Influenzae is the *usual* cause

(c) The onset is *typically* insidious

(e) Drooling is a *typical* sign.

Answers

(a) **True:** *Usual*, but not sole cause.

(c) **False:** Another inversion of the real situation; insidiousness is the opposite of what happens.

(e) **True:** Drooling occurs because the child cannot swallow, but though typical its absence would not exclude the diagnosis of epiglottitis.

Further illustrations of MCQ questions may be found in *Occasional Paper 46* (RCGP, 1990) and in *MRCGP: MCQ Practice Papers* by Peter Elliott (1993) published by Pastest.

Some Questions from Recent MEQ Papers

These examples are chosen to show the range of topics which may be examined and the ways in which the questions are set. They are taken from the October 1992 and May 1993 papers.

Examples 1, 2 and 3

These examples illustrate some questions in clinical topics.

1. During morning surgery you see Mrs Fiona Watt. You confirm she is seven weeks pregnant after trying to conceive for two years. All appears normal. She tells you that she wants to do "all the right things" and asks what sort of food she should eat.

How would you respond?

2. Mr William Silver, aged 64, consults you about generalized pruritus which he attributes to termites burrowing under his skin. The notes reveal that he has seen many other doctors about this problem. No evidence of infestation has ever been found and in the past he has angrily refused psychiatric help. Today you examine under the microscope particles which he says are termites but which prove to be amorphous skin debris.

How would you attempt to bring this consultation to a satisfactory conclusion?

3. George McPherson, a middle-aged man, comes and asks you to do something to help his wife, Agnes. He says she spends most of the day in bed, neglects her personal care, and is often found in tears. Mr and Mrs McPherson are both registered with you.

What could you do?

Examples 4, 5 and 6

These examples illustrate some questions on topics examining management of a practice, professional values, and relationships with colleagues and fellow workers.

4. After morning surgery one of your partners announces that he refuses point-blank to offer 'over 75' checks to any of his elderly patients.

What are the implications of this?

5. During an evening partners' meeting one partner, who has been in practice for four years, discloses that she has been asked to consider standing for election to the local medical committee. She asks for the partnership's views in order to help her decide whether or not to accept nomination.

What issues are raised by this suggestion?

6. Fay F, a young married patient of yours, consults you on a 'non-medical matter'. Fay is a friend of the new receptionist you have recently appointed and who will soon be starting in post. Fay has had two terminations of pregnancy and asks you to keep the notes away from the general storage area, so that her friend shall never learn of them.

What dilemmas are raised, and how would you resolve them?

Examples 7 and 8

Examples 7 and 8 were both the last questions in their papers and were perhaps a surprise to candidates. One deals with a new concept in general practice, and the other with the general practitioner's responsibilities in events outside the practice itself.

7. At a practice meeting Kay, the practice manager, tells you of an article in a medical magazine describing how a practice similar to this one had found benefit in the doctors, nurses, health visitors, practice manager and reception staff going away together on a 'team-building weekend' led by a trained facilitator. She suggests this might be a good thing for the practice to do and circulates copies of this article.

Describe how you would decide whether to follow up this suggestion, and what use might be made of such an idea.

8. A gas explosion occurs two streets away from your surgery, while the doctors are all present, and demolishes several homes. It transpires that an elderly lady has been killed and four other people injured, one of them seriously.

Describe the general practitioner's role in the community response to this disaster.

Some Questions from Recent CRQ Papers

The form of the CRQ has been changed recently so no precise examples of the new form are yet available. The principle of the questions in each part will be illustrated by these questions from October 1991, May 1992, and May 1993.

Part 1

Questions in Part 1 are to examine familiarity with contemporary literature.

Examples 1 to 5

1. How might you reduce your prescribing of benzodiazepines? Justify your answer with reference to your reading.

2. Comment on the health problems of the inner city homeless with reference to the appropriate literature.

3. Is cholesterol screening in general practice worthwhile? Summarize the current thinking with reference to the literature.

4. "Most pregnant women could safely deliver without the care of a specialist obstetrician." Discuss with reference to the literature.

5. Discuss the evidence concerning the detection and management of depression in general practice.

Part 2

Questions in Part 2 are to examine comprehension of written material and data presented.

Examples 6 to 10

6. **Reference:** The inflammatory smear: a study in general practice. (Kelly BA and Black AS (1990) *British Journal of General Practice* **40**, 238–40.)

The authors suggest that "all women whose smears are reported as *severely inflamed* should be treated with metronidazole and anti-fungal pessaries".

Comment on the authors' evidence for this statement. What are the implications for general practice?

7. **Reference:** Diagnostic and therapeutic efficacy of barium meal examination: a prospective evaluation in general practice. (Conry BG, McLean AM and Farthing MJG (1989) *British Medical Journal* **299**, 1443–5.)

Comment on the recruitment of patients for this study.

List the conclusions drawn by the authors. To what extent is each justified by the results?

Comment on the issues concerning the use of radiology services by general practitioners.

(*Note:* Three questions were asked in this 'old-style' question. Now only one would be asked.)

8. Mrs Smith sees you in surgery and presents you with this letter:

"Dear Mrs Smith

I write to inform you of the results of the needle test and x-rays of your breast. The needle test shows no significant abnormality but leaves a little doubt. The x-rays are likewise inconclusive. There are two options, one to undergo a biopsy of the suspicious area in your right breast, or to repeat the x-rays in a further six months' time. Perhaps you could let me know which of these you prefer.

Yours sincerely

Mr Brown
Consultant General/Vascular Surgeon"

You have not heard from the hospital. How might you deal with the issues raised?

9. These are the immunization figures from a practice of four full-time principals who operate a personal list system:

Doctor	A	B	C	D
Children aged 2–3 years	16	26	34	24
Complete course of:				
Tetanus/Polio/Diphtheria	16	25	33	22
Pertussis	14	13	32	21
Mumps/Measles/Rubella (MMR)	16	24	32	22

Calculate the overall percentage of uptake of immunization for children aged 2–3 years and comment on its significance for NHS target payments.

Comment on the immunization rates achieved by Dr B and Dr C.

10. What conclusions may be drawn from the audit of night visits done by a partnership of four doctors, as shown here?

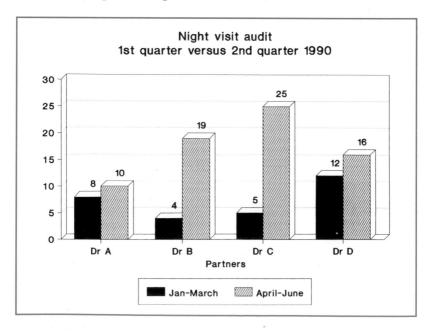

Index